WILD ABOUT
Sheen and Mortlake

FROM THE PARK TO THE RIVER

We are proud to be recognised as the Longest Established Independent Estate Agent in East Sheen and delighted to celebrate this association with the area by presenting this portrait of East Sheen & Mortlake in conjunction with the distinguished local photographer and writer, Andrew Wilson.

The directors and staff at Dixon Porter have over 70 years of combined and successful property and estate agency experience in the area. Our enthusiastic and extremely knowledgeable team is dedicated to promoting the many benefits of living in East Sheen & Mortlake with its varied architecture, wide open spaces of Richmond Park and Palewell and East Sheen Commons, riverside setting and highly regarded schools along with a vibrant and viable shopping centre.

We hope that this beautiful book will offer a further insight to the local attractions, some you will know well and others that you may have passed by unnoticed.

DIXON PORTER d p

INDEPENDENT PROPERTY PROFESSIONALS

202 Upper Richmond Road West, East Sheen SW14 8AN
020 8878 2828   dixonporter@btinternet.com   www.dixonporter.co.uk

Clockwise from top right: Stag in Richmond Park, Chiswick Bridge, The War Memorial and St Mary's Church.
The map on the end papers is taken from John Rocque's famous London Map of 1746.

Contents

Welcome to Wild About Sheen & Mortlake

Welcome to my latest collection of photographs. I have had my eye on this area for some time, not just because it is on my doorstep but also because of family connections. East Sheen for instance was where my father came to live with my grandfather in the thirties and where, after the Second World War, he set up his first home with my mother. Towards the end I made a fabulous discovery when I found that my father used to play tennis at the Sheen Lawn Tennis Club and that they had some old photographs of him that I'm sure my family haven't seen. As I write this, I am looking forward to showing my mum and my brother these when we next get together. As followers of my books will know I do much of my exploring in the company of my Springer, Josie, and this new book allowed us to venture to a couple of our favourite haunts, the river and Richmond Park, both of which you will find well documented within this book.

My books take some time and effort to produce but this is no one man (and his dog) show. I would like to take this opportunity to thank a few people for helping me. Firstly, Graham Menzies-Smith and the staff at local estate agents, Dixon Porter, who together with local solicitor Robert Cooles from Abbott Cresswell have kindly sponsored the book. I love nothing better than on a fine day taking myself off for a stroll with my camera and it is the financial help of local people like this that make it possible, so thank you.

I would also like to thank my chief writer, Helen Deaton and her husband David for their help – their deep knowledge of the area is second to none. I didn't know them until I started this book but I do hope we remain good friends. Speaking of words, I would also like to thank Tom Sears for his proofreading and to Silvina De Vita for her map. Further thanks should go to my designers, Tim and Dan from Ball Design and to my great friend and colour printing expert, Paul Sherfield. I may take the pictures but all these guys bring them to life. Finally to Isla Dawes from Sheen Bookshop who kindly commissioned this book and was chiefly responsible for getting me started in the first place.

My books take well over a year to produce and I meet many people along the way who have helped or contributed and unfortunately space does not allow me to mention you all, so my apologies if I have missed you off, it isn't personal. I have in many cases made reference to people within the relevant text, so if not here, you may well find yourself within the book. I hope you enjoy my latest publication; it was just the best fun.

Andrew Wilson, November 2013

Josie, my constant companion, racing through the grass in Richmond Park

First Edition – ©Unity Print and Publishing Limited 2013
Designed by Ball Design Consultancy *www.balldesignconsultancy.com*
Proofread by Tom Sears *www.tom-sears.com*
Printed by Headley Brothers of Ashford, Kent. *www.headley.co.uk*
Bound by Green Street Bindery of Oxford
www.maltbysbookbinders.com
Colour Management by Paul Sherfield of The Missing Horse Consultancy. *www.missinghorsecons.co.uk*
Published by Unity Print and Publishing Limited, 18 Dungarvan Avenue, London SW15 5QU. Tel: +44 (0)20 8487 2199 *aw@unity-publishing.co.uk www.unity-publishing.co.uk*

Mortlake and The Brewery from Dukes Meadows

Sheen and Mortlake

A SHORT HISTORY OF THE AREA
by Helen Deaton

Mortlake's history and character have been shaped by the Thames. There is evidence of much pre-historic activity by the riverside at Mortlake and the site undoubtedly had many attractions. Situated on a bend in the river and on slightly raised ground, there would have been clear views of boats approaching from either east or west; the river bed is of gravel, making it an ideal place for landing boats; fish were plentiful and the river supplied water for washing and cooking. But most importantly, the river provided a means of transport.

The Domesday Survey of 1086 refers to Mortlake as Mortlage. The name may have originated from the Old English; mort meaning a young salmon and lacu a small stream. In the 11th century there was a fishery in Mortlake which belonged to Earl Harold. The village could therefore have derived its name from its long association with fish or fish farming.

From before 1066 until 1536, the Archbishops of Canterbury held the Manor of Mortlake, a large and prosperous manor of some 8000 acres that included Putney, Wimbledon, Roehampton as well as the area now known as East Sheen. The manor house at Mortlake would have been an impressive building but it fell into ruin and now its foundations lie beneath the eastern part of Mortlake brewery. For some 500 years this important manor house and archbishops' palace received royalty (from King John to Henry VII), nobility, politicians (Thomas Cromwell was Lord of the Manor in the 16th century) and the highest churchmen in the country. They would have arrived by river from London or from one of the many other palaces on the Thames.

Queen Elizabeth I visited Mortlake on a number of occasions, not to see the manor house but to consult her astrologer Dr John Dee (1527–1609), Mathematician, navigator, Astrologer Royal and alchemist, John Dee lived in Mortlake for much of his adult life. His home, opposite the parish church overlooked the river. Dee would have found the royal palace of Richmond as well as Sir Francis Walsingham's estate at Barn Elms, easily accessible. Dee amassed some 3000 books and his library at Mortlake was, at the time, said to be the largest in Europe, making him an influential scholar. He is believed to be buried beneath the chancel of the parish church.

John Dee's house was demolished long ago but on the site of his laboratory Mortlake's tapestry works were later established. From 1619, under the patronage of James I and the Prince of Wales, highly skilled Flemish weavers were brought to Mortlake and created tapestries woven in wool and silk often enriched with gold and silver thread. The site of

Top left: This plaque in Tapestry Court marks the site of the Lower Dutch House.
Bottom left: A modern tapas bar recalls a piece of Mortlake's history.
Right: This block of flats named John Dee House was built on the site of Dr John Dee's garden.

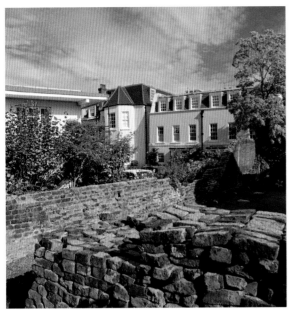

Left: Old bricks awaiting the rebuilding of this Tudor wall.
Right: This roundel, with the initials PW, is on the old wall of Mortlake Brewery.
It dates from 1869 when the brewery was owned by Charles Phillips and James Wigan.

the tapestry works by Mortlake's riverside was ideal, not only because the bulky raw materials could be transported with ease, but the high humidity was necessary for weaving. Sir Francis Crane was the first director of the works and Francis Cleyn the principal designer. They produced tapestries which were regarded as some of the finest in Europe. The tapestry works consisted of several buildings including accommodation for the workers, workrooms and a chapel. The factory closed in 1703 and the Upper Dutch House at 119 Mortlake High Street is all that remains of the complex. The site of the main tapestry house is beneath a pleasant grassed area and marked by a plaque. Many of Mortlake's tapestries have survived in museums and stately homes.

The land south of Mortlake's village centre, and stretching into what is now Richmond Park, consisted mainly of commonfields, a vast area that

was ploughed, sown and harvested for generations. However, by the mid 17th century large tracts were being worked as market gardens, providing London's growing markets with produce such as beans, peas, onions and asparagus. This trade reached its peak in the 1880s. In order to keep the fertility of the soil high, huge quantities of manure were needed. The solution was to send barges piled high with dung and night soil from London. This was unloaded at draw docks along the riverside. It was then heaped onto gardeners' wagons to be spread onto the nearby fields. Some market gardeners were still producing fruit and vegetables into the 1920s, and many local householders today continue to benefit from the tons of manure that had been added to their garden soil for 200 years or more resulting in a thick layer of rich black topsoil.

The first Mortlake pottery began on the site of a disused sugar house by the

Thames when John Sanders, a Lambeth potter, began making tin-glazed pottery in around 1743. The substantial volumes of clay for manufacture, and coal to feed the kilns, arrived by water. This company survived until the 1820s. However a second pottery works had emerged by 1800 which really established Mortlake's reputation for pottery. Joseph Kishere managed his small pottery works on Mortlake High Street making highly decorative salt-glaze stoneware. Kishere created hunting jugs, mugs, vases and other objects which are now highly collectable. Joseph died in 1843, Kishere's pottery soon closed and the building demolished 50 years after.

Malting in Mortlake dates back to the 17th century and the malt-houses along the riverside supplied many of London's breweries. Brewing has also been associated with Mortlake for centuries. Ale would have been brewed at the manor house from its very earliest days but it was not until 1765 that the first record of commercial brewing is recorded. Two small breweries then existed on Thames Street, the site of which now lies under the eastern side of the modern brewery. These two breweries combined and in 1852 Charles John Phillips bought them and went into partnership with James Wigan to form the hugely successful Phillips and Wigan brewery which expanded to fill the site east of Ship Lane. Again the brewery benefitted from the river, receiving huge quantities of hops and barley, as well as coal, by barge. In 1889 the Philips family sold out to Watneys which became Watney, Coombe, Reid in 1898. They developed the site to the west of Ship Lane to the size of the current brewery. In the 1960s Watneys employed some 1,400 men and women. It was not only the major employer but also provided extensive sports facilities, a convalescence home, housing for its workers, parties for children and a savings bank. Watneys ceased brewing in 1995 and currently Budweiser lager is brewed here.

The river has been used for commercial purposes for centuries, but it has also been a source of pleasure and sport. The first Oxford and Cambridge boat race from Putney to Mortlake was held in 1845 and, since 1856 has continued to be an annual event (except during the war years). The race finishes at a marker opposite Thames Bank with the seven-storey maltings building the final landmark on the course. The Mortlake towpath and The Ship in particular always attracting large crowds on Boat Race day.

The earliest recorded use of the name Sheen occurs in the will of the Bishop of London in around 950 AD. The bishop had lands there which were referred to as Sceon. The hamlet of East Sheen is referred to as Est Shenes in the 13th century. Until 1507 Richmond was called Shene; it was a royal manor centred on the Palace of Shene and when the palace was rebuilt by Henry VII it was renamed Richmond after the king's northern dukedom.

With no formal boundaries, opinion varies as to where East Sheen starts and ends. Historically East Sheen was a part of the ancient parish of Mortlake but it has in more recent times developed a distinctive character of its own. It lies on higher

Richmond Park deer holding up the traffic by Sheen Gate.

ground above the level of the river and so became a popular place for wealthy inhabitants to build their houses, well away from the damp and unpleasant air of the river.

By the early 17th century there were already several large houses in East Sheen. Temple Grove can be traced back to this time. It was a vast estate that originally covered some 300 acres and it later it became a highly prestigious school. Sheen House has been described as one of the finest buildings in the area, and certainly one of the grandest. Following its demolition in 1907, Shrewsbury Avenue, Muirdown Avenue and Richmond Park Road were built on the site. East Sheen Lodge was another early mansion. Its lands stretched to the walls of Richmond Park and the house attracted many royal visitors. On one occasion in 1911 five queens took tea on the lawns – Queen Alexandra, Queen Mary, Queen Ena of Spain, Queen Maud of Norway and Queen Marie of Romania. Percy Lodge in Christ Church Road and the Old Farm House in Fife Road

are the only pre-Victorian houses that survive in East Sheen today.

Will try and get a shot of the Old Farm House in Fife Road for here this morning plus how about the shot in Richmond Park of Sheen Gate with the deer crossing the road in front together with the plaque, which again, I will get this morning?

At the beginning of the late 19th century rapid suburban development dramatically changed the face of East Sheen. By 1939 almost all the land south of the Upper Richmond Road to Richmond Park was covered by suburban housing. The imposing houses with their large estates had gone. But East Sheen retains the atmosphere of a grand and elegant past with its substantial well-designed villas, tree-lined roads and generous open spaces.

Helen and David Deaton
Barnes and Mortlake History Society
www.barnes-history.org.uk

Founded in 1955, the Society promotes interest in our local history, holds regular meetings and events and publishes literature on local matters. For more information please contact them via their website.

Leyden House, on Thames Bank, is the oldest house in Mortlake.

Sheen and Mortlake

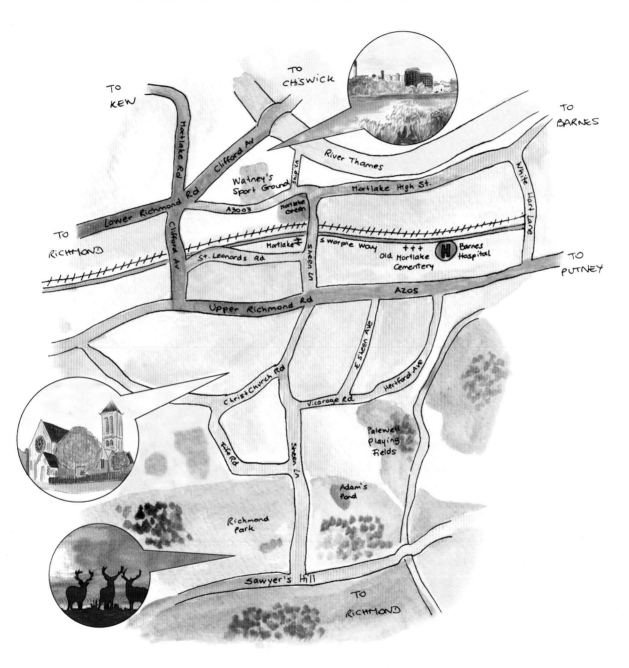

This map was kindly supplied by local artist, Silvina De Vita and is not meant to be absolutely to scale but to give the reader a fun introduction to the area and some of the places covered in this book. Silvina lives and works in Wimbledon and is a graphic designer and artist. She can be contacted via her website *www.silvinadevita.com*

Mortlake

Mortlake's early development was considerably influenced by its proximity to the Thames; it was along the river bank that the manor house was built, and the tapestry and pottery works were established. Most importantly for Mortlake, the brewery expanded into a major industrial complex that became an integral part of local life for more than 200 years, providing employment and social amenities for many local families.

The railway came to Mortlake in 1846 but left the shape and integrity of the village virtually untouched, along with its extensive network of passages and alleyways. Mortlake took pride in its thriving high street whose wide variety of shops catered for virtually all the needs of local residents. This was all lost to the road widening scheme along Mortlake High Street in the 1960s. The village now comprises many old houses that are to be found near to the river, the oldest being Leyden House on Thames Bank, but also purpose-built homes and converted flats and offices for those who live and work in what is still a tight-knit community.

Recognising that Mortlake needs some help, the local council together with the help and guidance of local councilor Gemma Stockley have created the Mortlake Uplift scheme, the first phase of which has been the work to improve the towpath between Mortlake and Barnes. Hopefully there is more to come.

Mortlake Green

Formerly known as Kings Arms Fields, the site was given to the residents of Mortlake by Earl Spencer, the Lord of the Manor, in 1860.

Previous page: A glorious display of crocuses on Mortlake Green in early spring.

The River

Previous page: Mortlake
at dusk from the towpath
from Barnes.

Above: Rowing is a huge
pastime on the river,
culminating in the Boat Race,
which finishes in Mortlake
(please see page 26).

Top: Chiswick Bridge through the Tideway Scullers School yard.

Bottom: Mortlake from Dukes Meadows one fine spring morning.

Far left: The river ablaze with late evening summer sun.

Left: A whitethroat – discovered on one of my many walks along the riverbank.

Bottom left: One of the houses that border the river, as seen from the towpath. Over the past year the local council have been making improvements to the towpath as part of the Mortlake Uplift scheme. This work is still underway, and when finished, a walk along the towpath will be a much more pleasurable experience and most certainly a less muddy one.

Bottom right: Mortlake from the towpath on the far side of the river.

Opposite: Chiswick Bridge from the shore, with a heron and some mallard ducks in the foreground.

Chiswick Bridge

Built on the site of a former ferry, Chiswick Bridge was opened in 1933. At the time it had the largest concrete central span of any bridge over the Thames.

Top left: A pair of canoeists at dusk from the towpath in Mortlake.

Bottom left: Mortlake and The Brewery one early morning from Chiswick Bridge.

Right: Mortlake from Chiswick Bridge late one evening.

The Boat Race

The Boat Race is an annual event between crews from Oxford and Cambridge Universities, which starts in Putney and finishes in Mortlake. Hugely popular and regularly attracting thousands of spectators along its route, the race was the brainchild of two student friends in 1829 – Charles Merivale from Cambridge and Charles Wordsworth from Oxford. The first race took place at Henley but moved to its current site in 1845 and, apart from the war years, has been held here every year since. In 2013 the race was won by Oxford, as can be seen in the main picture.

The Brewery

The origins of Mortlake Brewery can be traced back to 1765, when commercial brewing was first recorded on the site. For more detailed information please see Helen's introduction at the front of the book. A big thank you to Anheuser Busch InBev UK for allowing me access to take these pictures. In particular thanks go to Sara Conyers for setting it up and Rodger Parsons for taking me around. It was a fabulous day and as can be seen the views were spectacular.

Mortlake Brewery covers a massive 21 acres beside the Thames.

Left: Mortlake Brewery early one summer's morning from the far side of the river in Dukes Meadows.

Right: Mortlake and The Brewery in May 2012, as the longboats were practising their participation in the Queen's Jubilee River Pageant. This took place on the first weekend in June 2012. Unfortunately, the Queen was not lucky enough to have weather like this, as for those that remember, it was cold and wet and most unlike June.

Mortlake Fair

Mortlake Fair is a charitable event put on each year by St Mary Magdalen's Catholic Primary School Parent Teacher Association. Held on Mortlake Brewery's sports field, this year's event was on June 29th and thankfully the sun shone. As well as face painting, enjoyed by these lovely girls, I also met, amongst the many stall holders, Sandy from Cloverleaf Designs, who cleverly melds special four-leaf clover leaves into nice keepsakes.

Street Life

Left: Mortlake Brewery, as seen from the High Street.

Top right: The new look post office, so much nicer than the old one. It even has a bike stand outside that my springer, Josie, is modelling, very useful as there is a bike shop next door.

Bottom right: Boat Race House, one of the more recent developments that have sprung up alongside the river.

Opposite: One of the foot bridges that traverses the railway line that cuts through the centre of Mortlake.

Top left: Beware of trains; I love this sign found on one of the houses in North Worple Way.

Top right: Mortlake train station.

Bottom left: The infamous level crossing, where you can sometimes be kept waiting whilst five or six trains come by. There is a foot bridge, bottom right, for those that are in a hurry.

Left: One of the zebra crossings on Mortlake High Street, which takes you via a small tract of land, Tapestry Court, to the river, where part of the old tapestry works used to be; please see Helen's introduction for more on the history of the tapestry works in Mortlake.

Right: I particularly like this weather-vane found on a house along South Worple Way.

Far left: Church Path has many little alleyways, which date from when the area was just fields and these were paths.

Left: Beside the Old Fire Station at the top of Mortlake High Street where it connects with Barnes Terrace can be found this building with its fine fire escape.

Right: On one of my many explorations I discovered this attractive row of cottages called Rosemary Gardens, formerly the boot and shoe makers' almshouses, down beside the station.

Bottom right: Halfway along Mortlake High Street and on the river side can be found a small grassy park, Dovecote Gardens, where in spring can be found a spectacular ceanothus.

Top left: North Worple Way.

Bottom left: The bus depot at the top of Avondale Road. One of the excellent aspects of living in Mortlake is the 209 bus service, which takes you into Hammersmith. It's only a short distance and the service is good.

Bottom right: I like this postbox in a wall on Thames Bank by The Ship pub.

Opposite: These horse chestnut trees found alongside the Brewery's sports field have a show of wonderful pink flowers in spring.

Pubs

Left and bottom right:
The Ship, Thames Bank.
A fabulous location but the
road regularly floods at high
tide, sometimes leaving you
no choice but to have another
pint. As we went to press they
rather annoyingly repainted
the outside blue, looks good
but no chance to get a picture
like this again.

Top right: On the corner of
Ship Lane and the Lower
Richmond Road can be found
The Jolly Gardeners, which is
a reference to when this area
was full of market gardens.
I rather like the garden mural
on the side of the building.

Churches

With its distinctive church tower, St Mary the Virgin in Mortlake High Street can trace its history back to 1543 and has a particularly fine graveyard, with some beautiful flowering trees in spring.

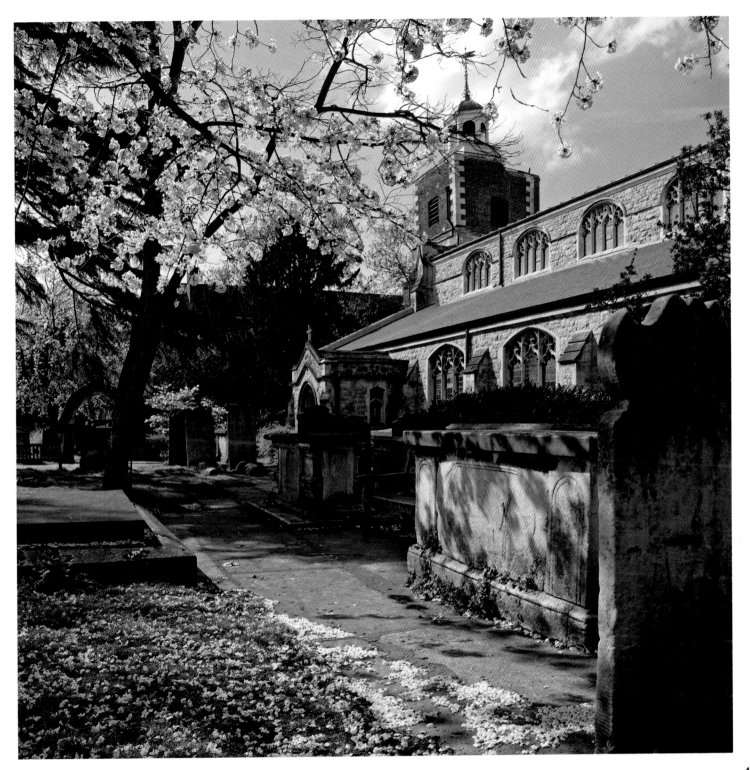

Bottom: St Mary Magdalen Roman Catholic Church Mortlake was built in 1852, with the school next door starting the very next year. Amongst other highlights is the extraordinary tomb to Sir Richard Burton, the famous 19th century explorer, which can be found in the graveyard (picture top left) and has been recently renovated.

Opposite and overleaf: The Old Mortlake Burial Ground, which can be accessed either via South Worple Way or Avenue Gardens, off the Upper Richmond Road looks particularly fine in autumn.

East Sheen

East Sheen's transformation into a London suburb in the early 20th century was rapid. As late as 1900 East Sheen consisted of a number of grand country houses in extensive grounds, several substantial Victorian villas, a few modest cottages and tracts of market gardens.

None of the grand houses such as Sheen House or Temple Grove remain but the distinctive atmosphere they created can still be felt in the elegant villas that were built on their estates. Several ancillary buildings and walls also survive, and a large number of the trees planted in the 18th and 19th centuries have now grown into impressive examples of cedars and planes. Many of the well-proportioned, good quality houses that were built in East Sheen in the 1920s and 1930s, such as those in Fife Road, were inspired by architects such as Edwin Lutyens. Several of these houses were also influenced by Charles Voysey's simple vernacular country houses but were built on a suburban scale.

The northern end of Sheen Lane was, until the late 19th century, little more than a narrow lane of cottages and commercial properties. It is now a busy street of small independent shops. The Upper Richmond Road had been a key thoroughfare for many centuries but developed into a major shopping street in the 20th century, providing goods and services for the expanding population of East Sheen.

Street Life

Opposite: The War Memorial in the centre of the village.

Top left: Upper Richmond Road looking east towards the crossroads in the centre.

Right: The milestone beside the War Memorial.

Overleaf: The centre of the village looking down Sheen Lane.

Bottom left: The Texaco petrol station, Upper Richmond Road West. I was fascinated to discover that our humble little filling station is in fact a Grade II listed building. Dating from 1926, it is one of the last remaining American-style filling stations in the country where the office and canopy are connected.

Upper Richmond Road

Far left: The Upper Richmond Road, as reflected in the window of Johnson's shoe shop.

The other pictures show the Upper Richmond Road as the sun sets early in 2013.

Opposite: The bikes outside BMG Scooters near Clifford Avenue.

Top: Mickey is the manager of Sheen Tyres in the Upper Richmond Road, which is a family run business established over 20 years ago.

Bottom: the bikes rather well lined up outside Basilico's.

Broadway Buildings can be found on your left as you approach the lights in the centre of the village going west. Here you will find Villa Rosa's and Leonardo's cafe, beloved by many a local. Besides the warm and friendly welcome, they also have a lovely garden, where I caught the two of them back in the summer, picture far right. Leonardo also has a wine bar and restaurant further up the Upper Richmond Road on the left past Waitrose.

This page: Robert Neil has been a fixture in East Sheen since 1972; a real family affair, Robert's two sons, Damien and Adam, and nephew Marc all work at the salon as do other family members, helping out on reception etc. A great bunch, they were only too pleased to pose for me when I suggested having a bit of fun with the poster they normally have in their front window; can you spot them top right?

Right: Just a couple of doors down from Robert's can be found Oh Darling!, which has a strange shape on account of the path that runs down beside the shop.

Left: Lucy the manager of Sheen Bookshop locking up after another day's work.

Right: Waitrose is always very busy and surely some of this success must be down to the stability offered by the management, Mike Jacobs for instance has been the manger here for over ten years.

Opposite: By contrast, Sura Wines has been on the Upper Richmond Road less than a year; having passed it on numerous occasions I just had to go in and take a picture of their wonderful window display, having admired it the first time I saw it.

Opposite left: Ron has run his fishing tackle shop for over 40 years. Now in his seventies you have to admire his tenacity, continuing to thrive when many others have fallen away; he is probably the only one left in South West London, he tells me. If you are wondering why he is holding up some cans of sweet corn, believe it or not it's fish bait, certainly a new one on me.

Opposite top right: A very stylish couple stride up the road in the late evening sunshine.

Opposite bottom right: Lee from another local landmark, Tony Swatland's butchers shop, opposite Waitrose. Besides making their own bacon, at the height of the BBQ season you will find that they stock over 50 types of sausage, a real mouth-watering thought. Love a good sausage!

Below: Deanhill Court can be found on the left as you leave East Sheen on your way to Richmond. Apart from being a very striking building, it also has a family connection in that it was where my mother and father first set up home in 1946 and where my eldest brother was born. My grandfather was the local bank manager and no doubt was instrumental in helping find them their first home; he also lived there at Number 38. I never met my grandfather but apparently he was an excellent bowls player, who played locally and was also picked for England.

East of the lights in the centre of East Sheen.

Top left: Sheen Uncovered and Ruby Blue next door are both run by Jackie Upton and her partner Anita. Set up in 1999, they apparently hold my wife's sizes just in case I'm in need of buying a present. I dare say this goes for many men in the area; good idea if you ask me. Jackie is also behind the local business organisation, East Sheen Village, which helps make the high street the vibrant place that it is. It's a thankless task, I know I help Chair the one in Barnes, so she deserves a huge pat on the back for all the hard work she puts in.

Bottom left: Sandrine's hand-made chocolates.

Opposite top: The Upper Richmond Road, looking east.

Opposite bottom left: Fat Boys Thai restaurant.

Opposite bottom right: I love the fish that the Sushi restaurant hangs out on the tree outside, very colourful.

This page: Adrian Hall Garden centre in the Upper Richmond Road, next to Gilpin Avenue. Every garden needs its flowers, so this is a regular haunt for many locals I'm sure.

Sheen Lane

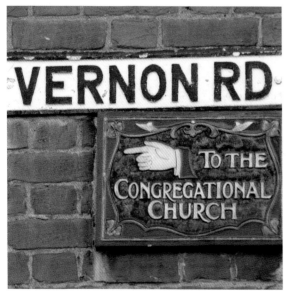

Opposite, top left and right: The nice garden of the restaurant Don't Tell Fred plus the window at the side, the only remaining evidence that this was once a department store called Rayner Canham.

Opposite, bottom left: The sign on the side of the building to the church in Vernon Road, which as of September 2013 was a brand new school.

Opposite, bottom right: The Old Bakehouse, off a little side road at the top of Sheen Lane by the junction with the Upper Richmond Road.

Top left: When Stewarts Pharmacy closed, its contents were preserved when Alex Mulholland donated the entire Victorian interior with over 400 artefacts and the original dispensing records dating from 1865, to Holly Lodge, Richmond Park, where they have been reassembled. The records show that members of the Royal Family who were living in Richmond Park, were customers. Ruth Mulholland has run her photographic studio from the premises since 2008.

Bottom left: Joe, who runs the hairdressers and perhaps better known as 'Hookah Joe'. During better weather he can be regularly found sitting outside on the street.

Left: The Sheen Lane Centre incorporating the library and a health centre.

Bottom, right and left: Pickle & Rye, the American style sandwich shop and cafe and Pandemonium the toy shop; this would a good pub quiz question, where might you see a skull and crossbones in East Sheen?

Opposite top: Nelson Cottages on Sheen Lane looking north towards the level crossing.

Opposite bottom: Classic car showroom.

Below left: The elegant office building on the south part of Sheen Lane with a smart tower and an even smarter weather vane, formerly the coach house of Sheen House.

Opposite top right: The lovely house on the corner of Sheen Lane, known as Red House, where it meets Vicarage Road.

Opposite bottom right: I have always admired the sun shades on this house, which is on Sheen Lane as it meets Stonehill Road.

The Avenues

Christchurch Road as it meets Fife Road.

East Sheen Avenue: this is my favourite of all the avenues on account of its magnificent line of trees and its also wider than the others, which shows off the trees better. I also discovered to my delight that behind the houses on the west side is a secret allotment (please see page 124).

This page: Vicarage Road, in spring (top right) and in summer, with its magnificent cedar tree.

Opposite: Fife Road has some magnificent houses, including this Tudor style one.

Left: The Dulux houses in St Leonard's Road, so named on account of their pastel shades.

Right: St Leonard's Court.

Schools

Top left and right and opposite: East Sheen Primary, which opened in 1913 as the Barnes, Mortlake Temporary Council School. In an eventful history its most dramatic moment was probably back in 1971 when following a break-in the school burnt down.

Bottom left and right: Richmond Park Academy. Formerly Sheen School, the school became an academy in 2010. Opened in 1927 as the East Sheen County School for boys, the school is currently undergoing a massive rebuilding programme, which is still ongoing as we went to press.

This page: Sheen Mount Primary School. Built on the site of an original large house, from which the school gets its name, one of the reasons for its local popularity must be its wonderful large grounds. It's interesting to note that a previous pupil was none other than Sir Tim Berners-Lee, the inventor of the internet.

Opposite: Tower House. Opened in 1932, this independent school for boys has four houses, all named after famous historical figures, Newton, Scott, Nelson and Shackleton. I wonder which of these characters inspired the comedian and ex-pupil Jack Whitehall the most?

Pubs

This page, top and bottom left and opposite: The Plough in Christchurch Road. Over 200 years old, this is a very popular pub amongst locals and visitors alike.

Right top and bottom: The Victoria in West Temple Sheen is perhaps better known as a fine restaurant than a pub, and dates from the mid-1800s. Taken over by the Michelin starred chef Paul Merrett in 2008, the place has since been returned to something resembling its old style and now boasts seven hotel rooms.

Opposite, top left and bottom: Hare and Hounds. Situated on the Upper Richmond Road, this pub dates from the time when there were horses rather than cars coming by, as it sports an entrance to a large back garden, originally designed for carriages etc.

Top right: The Pig and Whistle in Sheen Lane. According to the very useful 'Beer in the Evening' website, this used to be known as The Bull until 1987, when it changed its name.

Churches

Opposite, top left and right: Christ Church. As with many churches in South West London, Christ Church dates from the mid-1800s when there was an urgent need to provide a place of worship for the ever increasing local population.

Bottom: All Saints: this church on East Sheen Avenue dates from 1929 and forms a parish with the other two local churches, Christ Church and St Mary's (see page 48).

Open Spaces

The residents of Mortlake and East Sheen have for centuries enjoyed plenty of open spaces in which to walk, play and work, well away from noise and pollution. Common lands and market gardens meant that the area retained a rural atmosphere until the 20th century. Despite more recent housing developments, the wide roads, prolific trees, the cemeteries and Mortlake Green allow for pleasant walks and an opportunity for wildlife to flourish.

Two areas in particular became especially important for those who enjoy outdoor pursuits. Palewell Common was referred to as Pale common from the 16th century, so called because it was common land enclosed by a fence or pale. Its 30 acres became known as Palewell Common at the end of the 18th century. East Sheen Common was part of Mortlake common land prior to the enclosure of Richmond Park in the 17th century. Its 52 acres are now owned by the National Trust, and like Palewell Common it boasts sports fields and quiet woodland walks.

East Sheen Common

Left: A certain Diana Wilson, my wife, enjoying a day out in the snow with our daughter, Amy.

Previous page: East Sheen Common in autumn.

East Sheen Common in autumn can be spectacular in the right light.

This page: After the drought conditions of early 2012, the rest of the year and into 2013 there seemed nothing but rain, which resulted in the common being flooded for several weeks in early spring 2013. This particular bench would not have been your choice back then but there are plenty to choose from. I was fortunate enough one summer's evening to bump into a local lady sitting on the one top right and left, Zora, and as we admired the fantastic sunset she explained that she had commissioned the bench herself to commemorate her late husband, Derek, who was very fond of this place. She also had the tree placed beside the bench to offer its occupants a little shade, how wonderful.

This page: A regular sight in the summer; I was enjoying taking some pictures of the cricket one afternoon and decided to try and get a close-up of the action and got somewhat more than I bargained, namely the very last ball of the match – the stroke looks good, its just a shame he missed the ball.

This page: Near East Sheen Common and just off Fife Road can be found Sheen Lawn Tennis and Squash Club, which was founded in 1921. As you will know from reading the entry on page 71, my parents lived in East Sheen just after the war (and my father before it too). Well something I didn't know until researching this book, was that my father was a good tennis player and this was his club. One memorable moment, my mum tells me, was him winning the doubles at the Surrey Championships in 1938. Apparently he and his partner, L Wooton, were unbeaten everywhere that summer. I am grateful to Alex and Tony from the club for allowing me to access their archives where I have found many pictures of my Dad that I've never seen before.

Overleaf: some spectacular clouds on the common reflected in a puddle.

Gardens

One weekend each summer the gardens of Barnes, East Sheen and Mortlake open their gates for local people to come in an admire. Well as you'd have it, the day itself was awful and absolutely no good for taking decent pictures but I asked one or two owners if I might come back and take some on a better day.

Opposite: Arrabella from Fife Road has just had her garden re-landscaped but I was more taken with the magnificent cedar trees she has. Besides the lovely garden, Arrabella also told me that she had heard that Roger Waters from Pink Floyd used to live here – not sure if it is true but it's a nice story, I like the band.

Right: Also in Fife Road; perhaps a little more modest than some in this fabulous road but no less charming – thank you to Shirley and Geoffrey for letting me in and for introducing me to another couple in Fife Road (see overleaf).

Opposite: Fife Road. This was a fabulous garden, which runs all the way down to the wall that adjoins Richmond Park. They kindly look after a hive of bees for a lady that has an allotment behind East Sheen Avenue (see page 124).

This page: East Sheen Avenue – this was a sweet garden but more importantly, the access point to the secret allotments (see page 124). Thank you to Alex and John for letting me in; I did enjoy the more exotic plants they have, particularly what looked like little cactus plants growing on the handle of an old gardening fork.

Allotments

This and the next six pages:
Hertford Road. They had their open day on May 12th and thankfully the sun shone. Besides all the wonderful flora and fauna (and the beer and burgers that were on offer) I also discovered one of their resident robins had built its nest in a BBQ that had been left around, which came as a bit of shock for the owner when he came to clean it out. Please see the pictures on the top of this page, where you can just spot the tail of one of the adults protruding from the BBQ whilst feeding the young and pages 122 and 123. Thank you to Alex and Simon for being so welcoming.

Hertford Road Allotments:
I love the quirky things you see
in an allotment, scare crows
and listing sheds amongst
them plus the odd butterfly,
in this case a speckled wood.

These pictures were taken at the secret
allotments off East Sheen Avenue, where
amongst the fruit and veg can be found
some lovely chickens. Thank you again
to Alex and John for letting me in.

East Sheen Cemetery

East Sheen Cemetery can be reached off a road just past the entry to Sheen Common Drive on the Upper Richmond Road. The colours in autumn can be truly spectacular.

East Sheen Cemetery in January 2013. Here you can find wonderful views across to Richmond (bottom right) where St Matthias Church can clearly be seen on the horizon.

Palewell Common and Fields

Palewell Common and Fields were taken over by the council in 1921 at the bequest of the locals, who wanted to save it from development. A fabulous space, it has a vast open area for football and other sports, some tennis courts, a playground and a pitch and putt course plus a cafe.

Pictured here in January 2013 and in the summer overleaf. I am grateful to the website belonging to The Friends of Palewell Common and Fields for the background information and the surprising news that their used to be a pond here, amongst the trees at the entrance off Park Drive. However, they don't say when it was filled in.

Football and pitch and
putt are just some of
the activities enjoyed
on Palewell Common.

Ride London

Cycling events in 2012 were so popular that it was decided to try to repeat the success with an annual event, christened Ride London and sponsored by Prudential. Using roughly the same route, Sunday 4th August was the chosen date and the cyclists entered East Sheen via Clifford Avenue and then along the Upper Richmond Road, turning sharp up Sheen Lane and into Richmond Park. I am grateful to Philip Baum for letting me use his office for the shot far right; felt I needed an elevated site and his was the best, given little or no tree interference. It was very game of him and his wife to do this, especially as it was 7.30 on a Sunday morning. As I followed the cyclists up into The Park I was accompanied by this family, although they didn't know it and they kept appearing in my shots, culminating in the shot bottom right up on Sawyers Hill. I did love their good luck sign and their flag of course.

Over 20,000 cyclists took part in Ride London, as well as 150 elite riders from across the world. Hopefully these pictures give you a flavour of just how many that is, as they climb Sawyers Hill in Richmond Park.

Richmond Park

The southern part of Mortlake parish, some 650 acres, lies in Richmond Park. It is a Site of Special Scientific Interest and a National Nature Reserve as well as being by far the largest of the Royal Parks and home to more than 600 adult red and fallow deer. Surrounded by high walls, its 2500 acres are accessible through eleven gates.

English kings and queens had for many centuries hunted in the woods around Richmond. In 1625 Charles I brought his court to Richmond Palace to escape the plague in London and by 1637 he had turned this area of medieval farms and ancient pasture into a royal park. Charles enclosed his New Park with a wall, some eight miles long. The residents of Mortlake lost a large part of their common lands, and the Mortlake Vestry was particularly aggrieved as it did not receive any compensation from the king. However some public roads were kept open and villagers were allowed to gather firewood.

But in 1751 Princess Amelia (second daughter of George II) became Ranger of Richmond Park and closed the Park to everyone except her personal friends. This was a great inconvenience to many local people and caused a public uproar. In 1757 a Richmond brewer, John Lewis, took the matter to court. The case for pedestrian access was won and ladder stiles were put up at Sheen Gate and Ham Gate.

Richmond Park became a part of the Crown estates in 1851 and from 1872 all restrictions concerning access were lifted. A plaque was put up in 2008 at Sheen Gate commemorating John Lewis and his successful court action which opened up the magnificent Park to all.

Sheen Gate

East Sheen's very own entrance to Richmond Park in early spring, below.

Top right: Unfortunately, the nest of the pair of swans on Adam's Pond near Sheen gate failed this summer, 2013, and these were taken in 2012.

Bottom right: The large Beech tree by Sheen Gate can look fantastic in autumn.

Opposite, top and bottom left: Adam's Pond at Sheen Gate.

Opposite, bottom right: The postbox just outside the gate on Fife Road.

Right: The very familiar tower on the house opposite Sheen Gate, which I noticed has been put up for sale as we went to press on the book.

FIFE ROAD

The Seasons

Winter in Richmond Park

Left: Walking the dog on a frosty morning, with Broomfield Hill in the distance.

Right: Near Sheen Gate, looking across towards Sheen Cross Wood.

Overleaf: Early morning at The Leg of Mutton Pond, near Pen Ponds.

145

Left: Taking an early morning stroll near the Pond Plantation.

Opposite, top right: An amazing frost on the fence around Adam's Pond, Sheen Gate.

Opposite, bottom right: Cycling on the road that traverses the Park from the car park at Pen Ponds to Ham Gate, with the Isabella Plantation in the background.

Opposite: Beverley Brook near Roehampton Gate.

Top right: Deer near Isabella Plantation.

Bottom right: Kidney Wood, near Richmond Gate.

Above: Queen's Ride, looking towards White Lodge, the home of The Royal Ballet School.

Opposite top: A couple of jackdaws.

Opposite bottom: A pair of swans on the ice at Pen Ponds.

Left: Beverley Brook near Roehampton Gate.

Top: As I was taking pictures of this magnificent stag near the Isabella Plantation this gentlemen walked past and I really don't think he noticed the stag or he certainly didn't turn or stop and look, bizarre.

Bottom: My springer, Josie, eyeing up the rabbit holes near the Riding Ring on Sawyers Hill.

Opposite: The woods near Robin Hood Gate.

Top: Crows in early morning light near Robin Hood Gate.

Bottom: Some lads I captured enjoying themselves one summers evening on the logs that you find as you climb the hill away from Sheen Gate car park.

Overleaf: Sunset on the path that leads to Bog Gate and Sheen Woods.

Opposite: Beverley Brook in spring.

Top: A storm recedes from Tercentenary Plantation, near the car park at Pen Ponds.

Bottom: 2013 continued much as 2012 with lots of rain, which caused much of the woods near Robin Hood Gate to flood.

Opposite: To celebrate the fact that the Olympics of 2012 came through The Park, the authorities put up some wonderful flags on Sawyers Hill. The Shard and City of London can be seen in the distance.

Top right: A leaping fallow deer.

Top left: The bridge over Beverley Brook near Roehampton Gate.

Bottom: A wonderful kingfisher on Beverley Brook.

Deer

Opposite top and below: Red deer near Spankers Hill wood.

Opposite bottom: Red deer in Duchess Wood.

Overleaf: Red deer stags.

Previous page: A group of fallow deer early one morning, with Broomfield Hill in the distance.

This page: Red deer fighting.

The Day the Queen came to the Park

As part of the Queen's Jubilee celebrations in 2012, there was a large party in the park.
Fun was had by all despite the torrential downpour that occurred half way through her visit, see
overleaf; thankfully, even though well into her eighties, the Queen can still smile through adversity.

Isabella Plantation

This special feature of the park, which is known for its spectacular display of azaleas in April and May, see overleaf, can trace its roots back to 1831, when Lord Sidmouth, the then deputy park ranger, started transforming the area into what we know today. It was he that fenced it off but it wasn't until the 1950s that the beautiful trees and shrubs were planted by the then park superintendent and his chief gardener.

Peg's Pond in winter.

Top: A frozen robin checking out the sign at Peg's Pond. Sadly, I didn't have any food with me that day, which taught me a valuable lesson that in times of hardship if you want to attract the wildlife have something they can eat on you.

Bottom: A frozen Thomson's Pond.

Opposite: The wonderful Still Pond in May 2012.

Life on and around
Pen Ponds.

Top and opposite: Pen Ponds early one spring morning.

Bottom: Feeding the seagulls on Pen Ponds one winters evening.

JACK WATTLEY
DISCUS
FOR THE PERFECTIONIST

These discus varieties raised in Singapore at the Gan Aquarium Fish Farm were derived from turquoise stock originated by Wattley. Photo courtesy of Dr. Clifford Chan.

Dedication

This book is for those discus hobbyists who want more than just to keep their discus alive. It is for those who want to approach perfection in their culture and, in turn, perfection in their fish.

The author, Jack Wattley, with the Japanese discus expert S. Onya-san, who also translated for Wattley.

JACK WATTLEY
DISCUS
FOR THE PERFECTIONIST

MY SINCERE THANKS TO DR. CLIFFORD CHAN, DR. EUGENE NG AND THE GAN AQUARIUM FISH FARM IN SINGAPORE FOR SUPPLYING MANY PHOTOGRAPHS OF GREAT DISCUS.

TABLE OF CONTENTS

Introduction

When I reflect and look back to my initial trip to the Amazon, I suddenly realize how "international" discus have become. The major discus collecting areas are in Colombia, Peru, and Brazil - minor areas are found in Venezuela. But today discus are being bred successfully in America, Europe, the Orient, and even in Africa. No more is it necessary to endure Amazonian trips under conditions of strenuous trails, hand-over-hand clamboring, coupled with exposure to the frequent and unpredictable downpours.

Those of us who have made these trips are certainly aware that "new blood" must be introduced into the worldwide discus breeding programs. This can be done, of course, by obtaining imports, or by venturing into the Amazon Valley to collect the discus. Please count me out of any more collecting trips!

With discus becoming "international" I continually find in my mail letters from all parts of the world. Today as I write this I look at a "discus letter" from Sheffield, Tasmania! Another letter arrived recently from the Soviet Union. Many of these discus enthusiasts in different parts of the world find it nearly impossible to obtain current information about discus, much less to be able to obtain discus of good quality, or even of poor quality.

I must confess that I probably know as much about Germany geographically as I do about my own U.S.A. Why? Because I have visited innumerable discus breeders in nearly all parts of Germany. And without exception (sorry, except for one exception) all have been "simpatico", offering me to stay in their house during my visits, and showering me with their famous beer as well as their equally famous German chocolate cakes. All of these attentions and friendships brought about by an Amazonian fish!

A special treat. Being able to live with a Japanese family in Funabashi, Japan and to sample real Japanese home cooking - again, due to the discus fish. In Taipei, Taiwan the most gracious hosts, during a short stay. The hosts being discus fanciers. Discus hobbyists in Yugoslavia crossing into Italy to purchase and exchange fish, books, and magazines. Discus hobbyists traveling from Scandinavia and the U.K. to Germany for the same reason. A Spanish ex-bullfighter sending his American wife to Florida to purchase (hand pick) our discus. South African discus hobbyists traveling to Zimbabwe to gain experience in discus keeping with one of our respondents.

The finest hospitality shown to me by another of our book respondents from Auckland, New Zealand. His name was given to me by a discus breeder in Singapore. And still another book respondent - from Penang, Malaysia - much "discus talk" over dinner followed by a beautiful gift. The list could go on and on.

Discus seminars, which are principally held here in the U.S.A., attract people from many parts of the world, certainly due to the fact that most of the speakers are also from many parts of the world. At a recent discus conference in New York City, where I gave a discus presentation, there were other speakers from the U.K., Hong Kong, and Germany, as well as attendants from eight countries.

One country that merits special attention is Japan. Twenty years ago the Japanese had only *Symphysodon aequifasciatus axelrodi*, brown discus - and no breeding success. Five years later Bangkok blue discus made their appearance in Japan. Our Wattley Turquoise discus were the first pure strain of discus to appear in Japan, in 1980. My first discus lecture in Japan, with many more to follow, was in 1981. Today in Japan it is truly "DISCUS FEVER." The excellent Japanese "Fish Magazine" has an average of 45 discus ads each month, with articles featuring discus fish in most issues.

It is evident the fascination with the discus fish has spread all over the world. The interest in keeping and breeding of the discus can be found in the farthest corner of the earth. Language and political barriers do not stop discus enthusiasts in their quest. Indeed, the discus fish has played its part in fostering friendship among all peoples of the world.

Wattley visiting Wai Kee Aquarium in Hong Kong.

The author with Shirase in Japan.

Akimitsu Shirase, the great Japanese discus breeder, developed this strain which he calls the **Shirase Thunder Flash.**

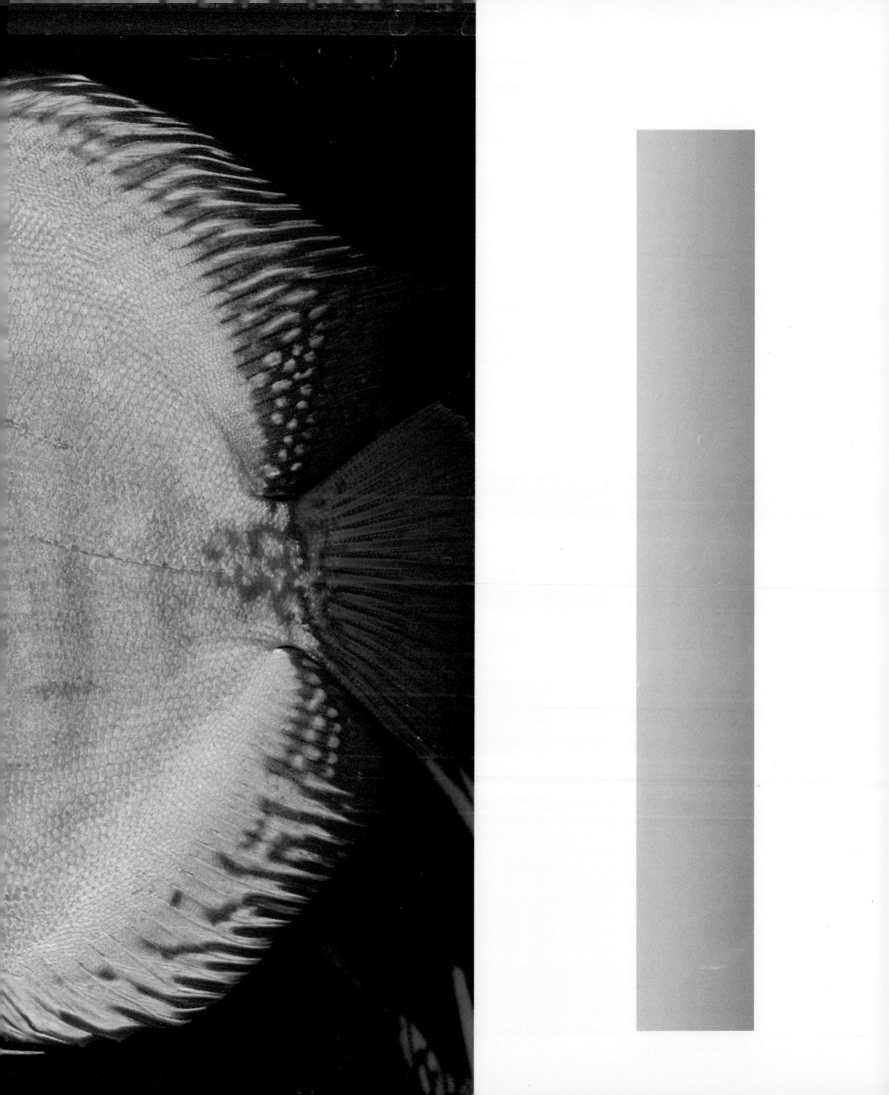

Very nice hybrid discus produced in Singapore at the Gan Aquarium Fish Farm.

Foreword

Mr. Jack H. Wattley's contribution to the discus hobbyist groups in Japan can be compared to that of Commodore Perry who came on board the 'Black Ships' and gave the opportunity to our country to open the door for international trade with foreign countries in the past.

The remarkable growth of discus fervor since Jack Wattley's first visit to Japan is the proof.

He is really a scholar of great research in the breeding of discus and his passion poured into the technical improvement of artificial breeding of discus is endless.

His conversation, each time of my meeting, on the improvement of artificial breeding of discus is always filled with much interest.

He is always filled with captivating mystery, just like the beautiful discus he breeds.

Mitsuru Hirose

Wattley with Mitsuru Hirose in Japan.

About This Book

Reading this book is like visiting with many of the world's best discus breeders and asking them the fundamental questions of how to successfully maintain and breed discus fish. It also answers the questions: "How does the best breeder in my part of the world maintain and breed them?"

HERE ARE THE QUESTIONS I ASKED THEM.

PURCHASING DISCUS:
Q. What do you look for in purchasing discus?

FOOD:
Q. What food (foods) do you feed your adult discus?
Q. Do you feed your breeding pairs differently than other adult discus?
Q. Frequency of feeding and variations of feeding program.
Q. Any special vitamins and/or nutrients added to the food?
Q. Your opinion of live tubifex for discus.

WATER:
Q. pH for breeding pairs, adults, young and fry.
Q. Hardness (Karbonate Hardness, General Hardness, Micromhos, Total Dissolved Solids, parts per million)?
Q. Is pH or hardness varied at any time?
Q. Do you use tap water, well water, spring water, Deionized water or Reverse Osmosis water?
Q. Do you ever mix different types of water, and if so, when and how much?

Q. Frequency of water changes and what percent for pairs, adults, young fry?
Q. Water temperature for pairs, adults, young, fry?
Q. Do you vary the water temperature, and if so, when and how much?
Q. If necessary, how do you control chlorine or chloramines in your water?

LIGHT:
Q. How much light and for what duration?
Q. Is light varied at times?
Q. Do you use reflector lights over your tanks?

FILTRATION:
Q. What kind of filtration do you use for breeders, adults, young and fry?
Q. What kind of filter medium do you use?
Q. Are wet/dry trickle filters used in any of your tanks?
Q. What filter litre/gallon capacity per hour?
Q. Your opinion of peat in your tanks?

AQUARIUM:
Q. What size of tanks do you use for breeders, adults, young and fry?
Q. At what height from floor are most of your tanks positioned?
Q. Are your breeder tanks apart from the general room activity?
Q. Are any of your tanks planted with live plants?
Q. Do you keep any other genera of fish with your discus? If so, what kind?

BREEDING:
Q. Do you raise your discus fry in a natural way or by artificial means?

Q. If raised naturally, at what age do you generally remove the fry from the parents?

Q. With fry mortality highest after removal from parents, what steps do you take to remedy this?

Q. What spawning medium do you use (PVC, flower pots, plants, bricks, etc.)?

Q. What steps do you take to induce spawning?

Q. How far in advance do you take these steps?

DISEASE:

Q. What disease do you encounter most frequently?

Q. What medications do you use most often, and for what diseases do you use them?

Q. What dosages do you use and in what time frame to effect a cure?

Q. Do you feel that pH has an effect upon the efficiency of the medication?

Q. What treatment do you consider best for *Spironucleus*, *Capillaria*, and flukes?

Q. Do you have any special "techniques" for saving otherwise doomed fish?

MOST IMPORTANT FACTOR:

Q. If you consider one factor of discus cultivation to be of more importance than any other factor, what is that factor and why is it of more importance?

Q. What special steps do you take on the matter?

LONG RANGE FUTURE OF DISCUS HOBBY:

Q. What views do you have regarding the future of the discus hobby?

NEW COLOR VARIETIES:

Q. Are you attempting to develop new color variations?

Q. If so, what direction are you taking?

FINALLY:

Q. Any points in this questionnaire that you feel have not been covered?

Wattley's discus, books and special discus foods are shown at trade fairs worldwide. This booth is a typical exhibit (Japan, 1990).

This is a very, very solid fish, with interesting color and a magnificent head. Produced by Gan Aquarium Fish Farm, Singapore.

PURCHASING DISCUS

What do you look for in purchasing discus?

Schmidt-Focke-Germany. Color of eyes. Respiration normal. Firm excrements.

Nakamura-Japan. Fish that are of full body. To swim normally. No deformations. Normal and stable breathing.

Reeves-USA. Most important factors are fish of thick bodies, alert, active, with light body color. A fish with dark body coloration, hiding in back of tank is stressed and probably sick. Fins must be erect, not clamped - respiration "smooth" and easy. A discus with a rapid respiration rate and exaggerated gill movement has some gill disease, which may permanently affect the health of the fish. If possible, obtain fish which have been owned for several weeks by previous owner. Quality of discus is difficult to determine. Some discus show bright reds and blues at an early age, and in many cases this coloration has been induced with hormones or color supplements. The blue coloration, hormone induced, is a preview of the fishes' adult potential. Hormones can't produce a color which the fish doesn't already genetically have. Red coloration in young discus is due to the feeding of high carotene foods - colors which will fade and not return. Look for good body shape in young discus. A long, oval body in a young discus will be a long, oval body in an adult fish.

Handley-New Zealand. Clear eyes. Excellent color. Round body shape. Normal respiration. Good appetite, with willingness to eat a varied diet (this point is very important).

Wong-Malaysia. Healthy and well proportioned discus, with normal light coloring.

Dollman-USA. I prefer to purchase young discus, under three months of age - with thick bodies, round eyes. I look for eyes that are sized in proportion to the fishes' body size. I favor young discus over adult discus because they seem to acclimate faster, and are more willing to spawn after they pair off than adult discus which I have obtained. (*J.W. I agree with his last point re purchasing young discus*).

Feiller-USA. I am extremely cautious in purchasing discus because of the different diseases and parasites that are so prevalent. Fry are purchased for the characteristics of their parents. I look for young from a set strain and not F_1 or F_2 hybrids. All F_1 and F_2s (50 percent of F_2 progeny) are dominant hybrids if parents aren't of same strain. I look for discus that are full bodied, erect fins, alert and that they have their nine vertical bars - not seven, eight, or ten bars. And that the bars are not crooked, which can indicate spinal deformities. I look for excellent color in the parents, as well as viability of the parents,

which will determine whether or not the progeny should be bred back to each other. I like to pick some of the larger fry, as well as some of the medium size fry to insure that I have both males and females. Normally, the males are the larger of the fry. (*J.W. I think fry must be at least 4.5 cm size before one can attempt to pick for males and females*).

Long-Zimbabwe. This is difficult to answer, being isolated as we are here in Africa. I have always tried to depend on breeders with excellent reputations.

Au-USA. I prefer to purchase discus only from reputable breeders. Better yet, visit the hatchery and observe the conditions of all the discus. Juvenile discus that are active with light body colors, erect fins, stocky bodies, and a willingness to feed tend to indicate good health. Selecting from a large group of similarly sized fish with relatively smaller eyes will insure against getting runts or culls.

Schulze-England. Round specimens with small red coloured eyes.

Jordan-Canada. Purchasing quality discus has been a never ending battle for me. I have visited breeders world wide looking for what I feel are "quality fish." My travels covered areas of Thailand, Singapore, and Hong Kong. Unfortunately, I was disappointed. The fish in many cases were the most beautifully coloured I have ever seen. Many had incredible electric blue and green hues unmatched by anything I have seen. However, when more research was done into the parental background and next generation results, I quickly realized that these discus were genetic flukes, or just in their genetic infancy. Also, I noted that many of these fish were far too inbred, therefore producing many genetic mutations or having a severe fertility problem in the males.

Gobel-Germany. I look for good round shape, good size of the fish, and small red eyes. Also, color of fish is important, with high, well developed finnage.

Shirase-Japan. That fish appear to be healthy, of firm, round body, with small red eyes. Fins erect, respiration normal, light body color. In the case of true species, the fish in question can be identified as such.

Chan-Singapore. There are hundreds of so called "discus breeders" in Singapore, but most of these have only ten to twenty tanks each. Most of these people breed with whatever discus that are willing to pair up. Few are highly selective. I prefer to obtain my discus from either large scale breeders, or American/German discus. The fashion in Singapore at the moment is keeping discus of hi-body/hi-fin. When I purchase discus I look for the following characteristics: at least four to five cm in size. I think hi-bodied discus can only be distinguished at such a size. Needless to say, the finnage must be balanced and the eye size

A pair of normally colored fish, fine quality. Produced by Gan Aquarium Fish Farm, Singapore.

proportional. I do not consider discus with a kinked forehead. This defect is fairly common and must be bred out. Some claim that the kink in the forehead becomes less obvious with age, but it is not worth the time and risk to find out. Always be certain the gill covers are adequate and cover the gills completely. This is a common defect which may not be so obvious to many. There are some discus whereby the dorsal fin is more posterior than it should be - these fish are of no value.

Chan-Singapore. Be sure the fish are non-hormoned. Choose the more colourful ones, being careful to exclude stunted fish - which are usually more colourful as they become older. Look at the colour of the parents. This gives some clue. A better indication of the type of discus you are buying can be obtained if you can actually get to see adult fish from the same parents. This understanding is not often possible unless the breeder has kept the entire brood. Usually only the best ones are kept by the breeder, so it may be misleading. Nowdays unscrupulous breeders add all kinds of colour enhancers to make the colours more vivid. Beware especially of the "red turquoise". Recently I saw a fish which was judged as a first - the fins and tail of this discus were all red in colour. Obviously it was dosed with red colour enhancing substances. Normal red discus may have a reddish tinge on their fins, but the tail will be transparent.

Yasuchi Nakamura, Narashino, Chiba, Japan.

A wild common brown discus, *Symphysodon aequifasciatus axelrodi.* This was the base stock of early discus. Photo by Gunter Schmida, with the courtesy of Horst Mueller. The fish below is a highly inbred, not-so-good quality genetically manipulated fish.

FOOD

What food (foods) do you feed your adult discus?

Schmidt-Focke - Germany. Frozen beef hearts free of hormones. Turkey hearts mixed with crab meat, spinach, and dry fish food. Also live *Daphnia* and live *Enchytraeus albidus*. Another excellent live food is the small white worm, Grindal worm.

Schulze - England. Mainly frozen bloodworms, frozen *Artemia*, black mosquito larvae. Also I feed lobster eggs, frozen beef hearts, and from time to time dry pellet fish food.

Au - USA. Finely chopped beef heart minced with multi-vitamins, shrimp meat and chopped spinach as primary food source. (*J.W. In my opinion, an excellent diet*). Periodically, clean live tubifex, white worms, and live brine shrimp are also used.

Dollman - USA. A beef heart mix that I prepare myself. I obtain one whole beef heart and remove all veins and fat. I run this through a meat grinder once. To this mix I add on raw egg, a pkg. of gelatin (unflavored), one tablespoon of paprika, and four tablespoons of a commercial *Spirulina* algae flake food. All of this goes through a blender until liquid. It is then spread out on a cookie sheet and frozen. Small pieces are cut off and fed to the discus fish. I also feed frozen *Artemia* and frozen bloodworms.

Jordan - Canada. 75 percent of the food offered to my discus is a beef heart mix which consists of: beef heart, shrimp, spinach, cauliflower, wheat germ, pears. The remainder of their diet consists of frozen bloodworms, plus live white worms and brine shrimp. (*J.W. I want to get back to Dale Jordan, re his adding pears and cauliflower to his discus diet - it sounds very interesting!*)

Wong - Malaysia. Live tubifex, ground beef and beef hearts, and ground pork.

Feiller - USA. I feed a complex beef heart based formula. The adult discus get the same formula that is fed to the fry. It consists of beef heart, shrimp, *Artemia* flakes, hi-protein baby cereal, baby pureed squash, peas, raw eggs, paprika, *Spirulina* powder, and gelatin. The gelatin is used to combine the ingredients. I supplement this in the evening with frozen blood worms for the adults only.

Gobel - Germany. Uncooked fresh beef hearts, frozen *Artemia*, frozen blood worms, frozen *Daphnia*, and live and frozen glass worms (*Corethra*).

Reeves - USA. I feed a basic home made diet, frozen, of two parts beef or turkey hearts, one part liver, one part fish, and one part mixed vegetables. As each batch of food is thawed it is

Tank-raised brown discus, *Symphysodon aequifasciatus axelrodi*, raised by Osvaldo Gonzalez.

C.M. Wong produced this turquoise discus.

This tank of discus gives an inadequate indication of quality. But they may grow up into outstanding fish. Produced by Harold Beck.
The fish below are Singapore's Clifford Chan fish.

supplemented with a variety of flake foods, freeze dried plankton. By varying each batch of food I hope to avoid any dietary deficiencies. The only other foods given are commercial flake foods or frozen artemia.

Nakamura - Japan. We feed discus hamburger (minced beef heart mixed with vegetables and shrimps.)

Chan - Singapore. In Singapore many types of food are fed. The older breeders tend to believe only in live tubifex and live blood worms. They religiously buy live food each day from the same source. When I first started with discus I fed tubifex exclusively. I got the worms from a well known "Discus Worm Seller," and I never had any problems with disease. The fish grew fast and were always hungry. I only stopped feeding tubifex because I got tired having to travel ten km to buy worms each day. Moreover, as I acquired more discus it became too expensive to feed them live worms. I always recommend to others that they buy tubifex worms only from a tried and true source. Occasionally I've tried using tubifex from other sources and have paid the price - dead discus. There are some who go as far as to soak the worms in antibiotics, but I am doubtful of its usefulness. The more educated hobbyists feed beef hearts. The usual preparation consists of about fifty percent heart, the rest is highly variable - tiger prawns, fish meal, chicken, beef liver, blood worms, koi pellets and

flakes. All of these are used. At the moment I'm trying out a new concoction involving egg and beef hearts, which so far has been very promising and produces fantastic growth rates in all my discus fish.

Long - Zimbabwe. I feed ox hearts daily, along with earth worms and *Daphnia*. When it is available I also use freeze dried tubifex worms. (*J.W. Why don't more of us feed earth worms, as Stephen Long does? Probably no better food for discus.*)

Handley - New Zealand. Beef hearts, white worms, and when available, *Daphnia*. (*J.W. When I visited Don Handley in Auckland several years ago he was feeding his fish a locally grown cold water type of tubifex worm.*)

Shirase - Japan. We use beef hearts as 80 percent of the discus diet, the other 20 percent of the time we feed frozen red worms (blood worms).

J.W. I'm surprised none of the respondents include frozen plankton in their discus diets. I consider it an excellent food. But I do see that most of the respondents do include a green food of some sort in the diets. In the wild, discus are omnivorous feeders, probably due to the fact that they're not migratory and they must depend on whatever food is available to them at any time. For that reason, Amazonian discus must have a broad feeding spectrum, feeding on plant material including fruit. I'm certain, after having examined the

The fish above is one of Manfred Göbel's discus. The fish below was produced by Shirase.

stomachs of discus in Colombia and Brazil, that they subsist on a greatly reduced diet compared to what they find in the home aquarium. This is especially true during times of low water, when they can be confined to very restricted quarters.

In the home aquarium discus food is mainly protein matter, which is necessary for growth, energy, and to repair body tissue. It's difficult to determine the exact carbohydrate requirements for discus, but as stated before, being omnivorous, we know plant material is important in the diet. As the respondents have stated, this can be in the form of spinach, lettuce (dark colored), algae, peas, etc., usually mixed into a beefheart diet. I've added banana - yes, I said banana - to the beef heart formulated diet I feed my discus and in one control test found I got an excellent growth rate feeding nothing but banana to a small group of three-week-old fry for a period of four weeks.

Over the years I have developed and improved our frozen formulas using a combination of beef heart, shrimp, liver, spinach, vitamins, and in one of the formulas, banana. Through hundreds of trial and error situations with my own breeding stock and young juvenile fish I have arrived at what I feel are the most effective formulations.

For achieving successful spawnings, I use a combination of my discus food and my conditioning food. To achieve the most rapid growth while maintaining optimum coloration and disease resistance, I use a combination of my community tank diet and again my standard Discus food. My "Fry Food" is a similar formulation, but ground into

a much finer consistency. I find I can begin feeding this "Fry Food" formula to the young discus at a size of approximately 3/8 inch.

Thanks to a recent development in the commericial fish food industry, my formulas will very shortly be available to hobbyists throughout the USA and Europe - with distributorships already set up in Germany and the U.K. I have recently made arrangements with Ocean Nutrition, Inc. to market four of my formulas to the tropical fish industry. I have listed below the names of these products as they will appear in the marketplace. Inquire with your local tropical fish store or pet shop as to availability, and if they aren't yet available locally, call me here in Fort Lauderdale, Florida (but not at 2 am), or Ocean Nutrition, Inc. in San Diego, California for more information as to where they can be obtained.

The Ocean Nutrition Professional Signature Series:
JACK WATTLEY DISCUS FORMULA
JACK WATTLEY CONDITIONING FOOD
JACK WATTLEY COMMUNITY TANK FOOD
JACK WATTLEY FRY FOOD

Do you feed your breeding pairs differently than other adult discus?

Schmidt-Focke - Germany. Yes, mainly live foods from ponds in my backyard garden area. This will consist of mosquito larvae, fresh water shrimps and *Gammarus* shrimps. Live *Daphnia* is also cultivated in the ponds.

Shirase - Japan. We feed entirely the same foods as we do all other discus we have.

Gobel - Germany. No!

Jordan - Canada. Pairs, young, and adults are fed exactly the same.

Dollman - USA. No. All fish fed the same.

Handley - New Zealand. No change in feedings.

Long - Zimbabwe. No.

Chan - Singapore. No.

Nakamura - Japan. Same as adult fish in most cases - other times we feed prawn eggs.

Reeves - USA. Breeding pairs are fed the basic variations of the frozen foods and *Artemia*. Other adult discus kept for display in community tanks are fed the same foods.

Feiller - USA. I feed all of my adults the same diet. All of the

adults are potential breeders or breeders on rest cycles.

Wong - Malaysia. No.

Schulze - England. No.

Au - USA. In order to keep water conditions more manageable, breeders tend to get more live food such as tubifex worms and live *Artemia*. Live food seems to promote spawning activities.

Wattley with Dick Au.

Typical advertisement for the Wattley Discus Formula.

Frequency of feeding and variations of feeding program?

Wong - Malaysia. Ground meal before the two major changes of H_2O and in between tubifex, *Artemia* and *Daphnia*.

Handley - New Zealand. In mornings and evenings I feed beef heart. Once or twice per week I feed white worms.

Feiller - USA. I feed at around 10 a.m. for the grow outs and adult tanks. The debris is syphoned out first and replaced with fresh water. Feeding again at about 7 p.m. The only variation is when I am not able to maintain the feeding program. Re the fry tanks, I feed three times per day. Fifteen years ago I had read that it was good to starve adult discus for one day a week so that the following day - after the fast - they would be very aggressive eaters. After several weeks of doing that it finally sunk in that they were aggressive eaters only because they were starving, and not because the fast had any therapeutic value!

Schulze - England. We feed the youngsters six to ten times per day, whereas the adults are generally fed three times daily.

Nakamura - Japan. Young discus under 2.5 inches are fed three to five times daily. For fish over 2.5 inches in size they are fed two to three times per day. Fish over one inch in size are fed only beef heart (hamburger). Sized below 0.7 inch, they are fed only *Artemia*. At size of 0.7 to inch fry are fed Artemia and heart.

Long - Zimbabwe. All adult discus are fed twice daily, six days per week. One day I fast the adults, whereas all young, growing discus are fed daily, three times.

Au - USA. For fully grown adults, I provide one feeding per day. Smaller fish are fed two to three times daily. In general, smaller fish get fed more often. Juvenile fish under four inches in diameter are strictly on prepared foods.

Reeves - USA. The frequency of feeding depends primarily on the age of the discus. Adult fish are fed three times daily, while very young fry are fed five to seven times daily. Fish being grown out as future brood stock are generally fed five times daily, until they are of breeding age.

Dollman - USA. Adults are fed twice daily. Young fish under one year old are fed three times daily, and fry under three months old are fed four to five times per day.

Chan - Singapore. Frequency of feeding should be at least thrice a day. Young fish should be fed as often as possible.

Schmidt-Focke - Germany. Four to five times daily, beginning with a dry food.

Shirase - Japan. For breeding pairs and other adult fish we change the frequency of the feedings as well as the quantity of food depending on their appetites.

Gobel - Germany. All adult discus are fed twice daily - each time with a different food. Our young discus are fed four to six times per day, also with a different food each time.

Jordan - Canada. Our adult pairs are fed twice daily. One feeding of frozen beef heart, the second feeding of frozen blood worms. The young discus are fed four times daily, consisting of seventy five percent heart, the remainder being *Artemia*, etc.

Any special vitamins and/or nutrients added to the food?

Schmidt-Focke - Germany. Yes, drops of multivitamins added to my beef heart.

Dollman - USA. I add a commercial liquid vitamin designed for tropical fish to my beef heart mix in the amount of one teaspoonful per five pounds of food.

Long - Zimbabwe. No

Reeves - USA. I use a multiple mineral pet vitamin when formulating my frozen food. No exotic food supplements are utilized at any time.

Wattley with Lo Wing Yat in the New Territories of Hong Kong.

On the facing page, top photo: A single fish does not mean a strain has been established. Lower photo: The school of young fish with quite intense green turquoise coloration, uniform markings and size, indicates a well established, successful strain.

Wong - Malaysia. Multivitamins, with added vitamins E, B, C. Fiber is added at times. Royal Jelly is added for all the adult fish. (*J.W. On Wong Chong Moh's suggestion I added some Royal Jelly to my beef heart mixed food, but I gave up on it too soon to see any results. I'm going to have to try it again for a much longer period of time*).

Au - USA. Yes. I use a liquid multivitamin for human consumption in the beef heart mixtures.

Schulze - England. Vitamin complex, in the heart.

Nakamura - Japan. I add small quantities of vitamin complex to all foods fed.

Feiller - USA. I do not add vitamins to the food. However, I do add liquid vitamins to the water.

Handley - New Zealand. Spinach or Silverbeet added to the beef heart.

Jordan - Canada. I use commercial mixes.

Gobel - Germany. No.

Shirase - Japan. We add vitamin complex as well as vegetables rich in chlorophyls.

Chan - Singapore. A vitamin complex, added to the foods.

Your opinion of live tubifex worms for discus.

Schmidt-Focke - Germany. No! Live tubifex have parasites.

Chan - Singapore. Yes, but as I said before, only from a tried and true source.

Feiller - USA. I no longer feed tubifex nor "black worms" in any manner. They are trouble. When fed to my discus the fish developed tape worms and were always having problems with gill flukes. Since the worms were deleted from the diet and the fish treated with a medication, the problem has never come back.

Shirase - Japan. Although tubifex worms are one of the better discus foods, I have no suitable place for them, nor the time to take care of them (to clean them), and for that reason I am presently not feeding them to my discus.

Au - USA. Live tubifex worms are a two-edged sword. I am convinced that they enhance growth and body color of discus as well as promoting spawning. However, I am equally certain that they are the source of many discus ailments. I only feed tubifex worms for fish larger than four inches in diameter and only after thorough rinsing.

Schulze - England. Never.

Gobel - Germany. Never live tubifex.

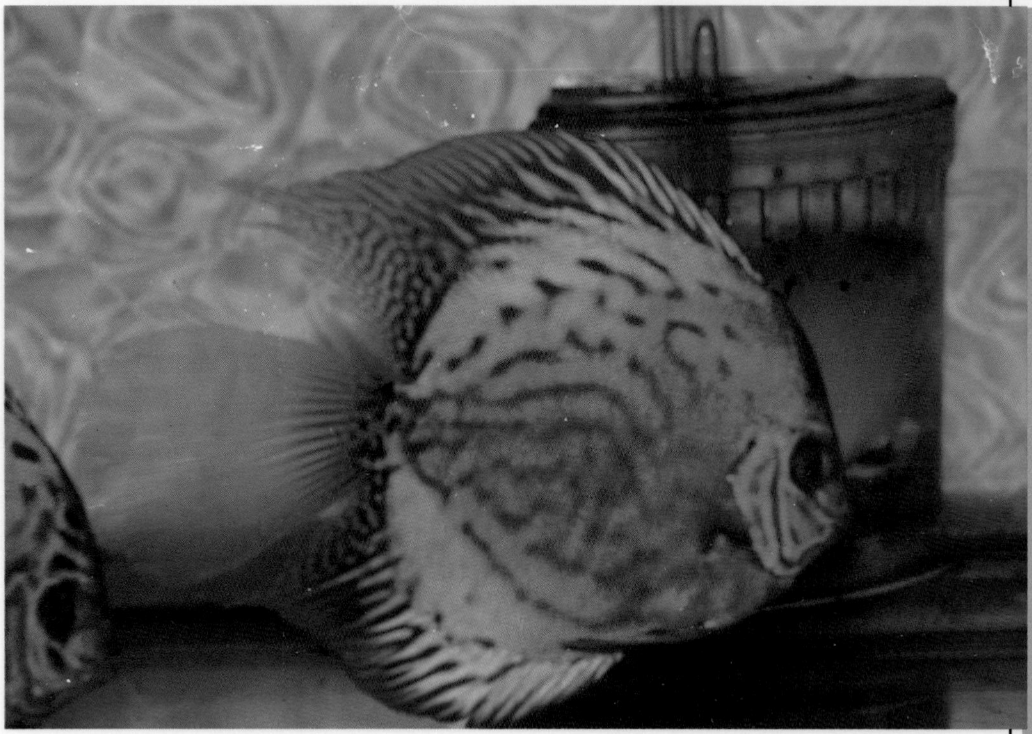

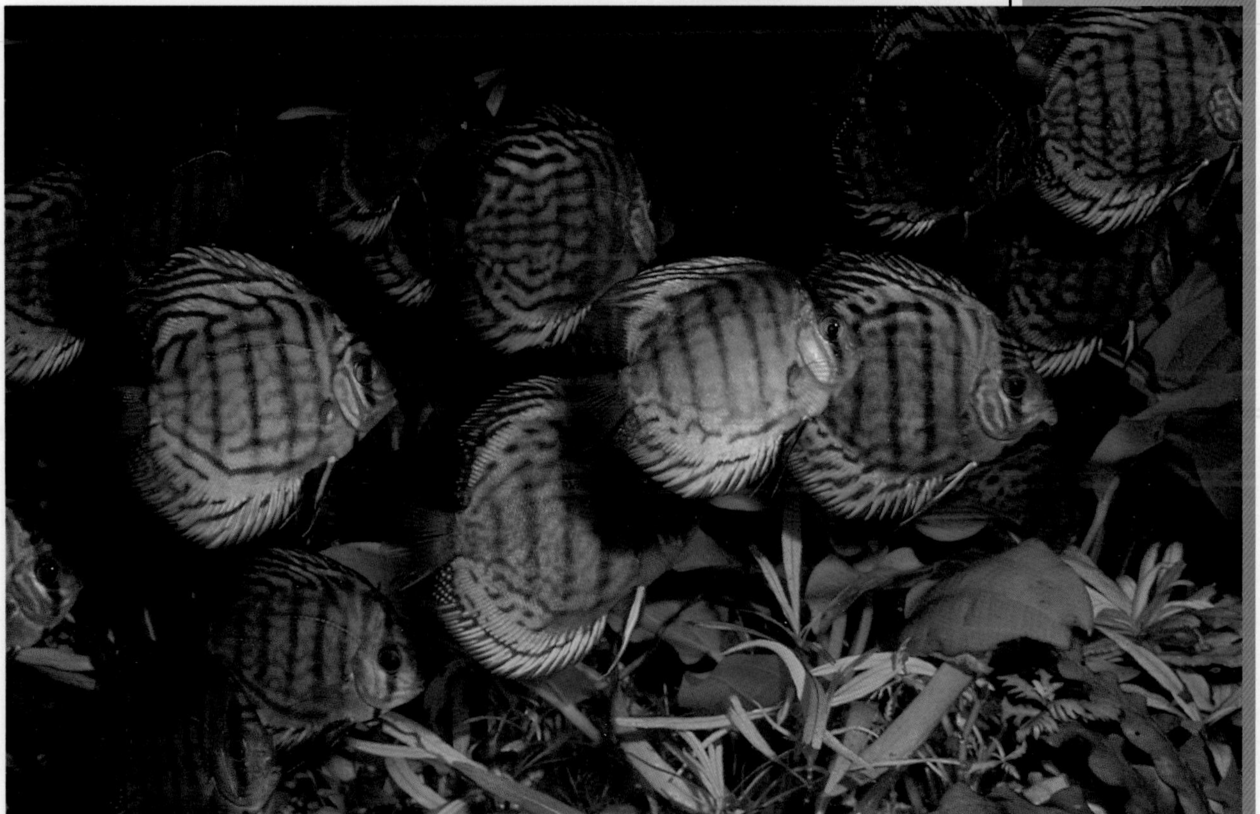

Jordan - Canada. I truly cannot argue the nutritional value of tubifex worms. However, the detriments certainly outweigh the benefits in regard to pathogens and parasites. Therefore, I do not feed tubifex except for the occasional treat.

Nakamura - Japan. Not desirable, as this food will bring in parasites and other pathogens.

Wong - Malaysia. Very nutritious, but the worms must go through at least forty-eight hours of continuous water flow before feeding.

Reeves - USA. I believe tubifex and black worms should be avoided when feeding discus. Cestodes (tapeworms) may be transmitted by tubifex and black worms, and I believe the red tubifex can be responsible for multiple bacterial diseases.

Long - Zimbabwe. Ten years ago tubifex was the only food I used. Today I do not feed tubifex. However, I never really saw any physical damage from the worms. And my discus did grow rapidly. But knowing what I know now, I do not feed tubifex worms at all.

Handley - New Zealand. If collected from a non-fish habitat and washed thoroughly for several days, OK. I feed one or two feeds per week of the worms.

Dollman - USA - I have never fed live tubifex worms to my discus, nor do I ever intend to, as I feel all of the discus dietary needs can be met with prepared foods.

A beautiful new color variation being developed by the Gan Aquarium Fish Farm, 4 Fish Farm Road 3 off Tampines Road, Singapore 1953. Fax: 285 1165.

From left to right: Dr. Clifford Chan, Manfred Göbel, Gan Kian Tong, (the main discus man in the Gan family) and Alfred Reiger.

WATER

pH for breeding pairs, adults, young and fry?

Schmidt-Focke - Germany. I maintain a pH of 6.0 to 6.5 for all my discus.

Dollman - USA. For breeders, a pH of 6.4 to 6.8. Young discus over one month of age a pH of 7.8 to 8.0. All fry, a pH of 6.4 to 6.8.

Shirase - Japan. For the breeding pairs a pH of 5.5 to 6.5. Other adults have a pH of 6.0 to 7.0. The young and the fry, a pH of 6.0 to 7.0.

Handley - New Zealand. pH for all my discus, pairs, adults, young, and fry - 7.0 pH.

Nakamura - Japan. For breeding pairs, in general, a pH of 6.8, but at the time of spawning adjust the quantity of water changes, so the pH will become 5.5 to 5.8. After the fry are eating newly hatched *Artemia* we raise the pH to 6.2 to 6.5 over a several day period. We are careful not to raise the pH over 0.3 at any given time.

Long - Zimbabwe. All my tanks maintain a pH of 7.0.

Jordan - Canada. For my breeding pairs (5.5 - 6.5 pH), young (7.0 - 7.5 pH), fry (7.0 - 7.5 pH).

Gobel - Germany. Breeding pairs pH 6.0 - 6.7. Adults and young pH 5.2-6.7. Fry pH 6.0-6.7.

Au - USA.   for breeding pairs, adults, young and fry, the pH from tap water in this region at about 7.0, and as the water ages in the tank it settles in at about 6.6 pH.

Schulze - England. All discus kept at pH of around 6.5 - 6.8.

Wong - Malaysia. Water in our area ranges from a pH of 6.0 to 7.5. We do not adjust the pH unless it is exceptionally high.

Chan - Singapore. (*J.W. I received no information from Dr. Clifford Chan re his pH*).

Reeves - USA. All my discus from fry to breeding pairs are kept in tap water, pH 7.2 to 7.4.

Feiller - USA. The pH for breeding pairs is between 6.0 and 6.8. The fluctuation comes from water changes (eighty-five percent Reverse Osmosis and fifteen percent tap water).

(*J.W. Has anyone ever determined whether or not the nutrients and micro-nutrients in the foods we feed our discus are more readily available at a particular pH? I haven't. But I do think someone could set up several control tanks, working with the same foods in each tank, maintaining a different pH in each tank, and monitoring the growth rate of each tank. I'd run the test for four weeks*).

Top: *Symphysodon aequifasciatus haraldi* **X** *Symphysodon aequifasciatus aequifasciatus.* Below: A tank with Harold Beck's lovely discus. All are well colored, finely shaped and showing great similarity.

Top: A Schmidt-Focke Turquoise **X** the so-called Bangkok strain. The fish was produced by Wong Chong Mok in Penang, Malaysia. Below: Wattley's fish are uniformly colored, grow at the same rate and are brightly marked. They reproduce true to type after having been inbred for so many generations.

Hardness (Karbonate Hardness, General Hardness, Micromhos, Total Dissolved Solids, parts per million)?

Schmidt-Focke - Germany. My tap water comes from the Taunus Mountains, and I adjust the Micromhos with some Reverse Osmosis water to 70 to 80.

Feiller - USA. Hardness about 30 ppm for breeders and adults. Reverse Osmosis water for the fry is not measurable in parts per million. I use tap water for the growth tanks, which is about 120 parts per million.

Chan - Singapore. Water used straight from tap.

Reeves - USA. I do not own any test kit or apparatus for determining water hardness. My basic tap water is moderately soft and I make no attempt to alter the hardness.

Schulze - England. Three (3) Degrees of Hardness one (1) Karbonate Hardness. Eighty to one hundred and twenty Micromhos.

Wong - Malaysia. Twenty to one hundred parts per million.

Gobel - Germany. For breeding pairs and fry Karbonate Hardness 0.2. General Hardness 2-4. Micromhos 80-120. For adults and young Karbonate Hardness 0.2-0.5. General Hardness 2.8. Micromhos 80-250.

Au - USA. Total hardness in water is between 25 to 50 parts per million. Total alkalinity is about 30 parts per million.

Jordan - Canada. Breeding pairs 60 parts per million total. 200 Micromhos. Young and fry 130 parts per million total and 570 Micromhos.

Shirase - Japan. General Hardness 6 and Karbonate Hardness 3.

Long - Zimbabwe. 60 parts per million expressed as Calcium Carbonate.

Handley - New Zealand. Forty parts per million.

Dollman - USA. Adults and breeding pairs and fry under one month of age 40 - 60 parts per million $CaCO_3$. Young adults and fry over one month of age 250 to 300 parts per million $CaCO_3$.

Nakamura - Japan. Karbonate Hardness below 1.5. General Hardness below 2.5. Micromhos 60 to 80. Total Dissolved Solids not exactly known, but probably below 20 parts per million at total hardness. I use the above mentioned water for breeding.

J.W. A quick breakdown re various methods of measuring hardness:

Total Dissolved Salts	Micromhos	Calcium Carbonate
25	37.5	15
40	60	24
50	75	30
66	150	60
250	375	150
400	600	250

Is pH or hardness varied at any time?

Schmidt-Focke - Germany. Not to any great degree.

Gobel - Germany. pH is varied from 6.0 to 6.7 for breeding pairs and fry. And from 5.2 to 6.7 for adults and young discus.

Handley - New Zealand. Very little.

Nakamura - Japan. During the breeding season and in time of ordinary management pH and hardness can be varied. The low hardness of the water for the breeders is very hard to control, because the drop of pH is too drastic.

Long - Zimbabwe. Not purposely.

Dollman - USA. I use tap water for all fry and young adults over one month old. Reverse Osmosis water and distilled water for adults and fry under one month of age.

Shirase - Japan. Yes, it is necessary especially for breeding pairs to change both the pH and the hardness.

Reeves - USA. The only variation of pH is the variation produced during my routine water changes - usually within the range of 7.0 to 7.4.

Feiller - USA. Hardness and pH are not varied other than what occurs by my water changes.

Chan - Singapore. No.

Au - USA. The pH of the water in tanks tends to slowly move lower days after water changes due to uneaten food or discharges from the fish. I make no attempts to alter the water chemistry by the use of chemicals or peat. However, frequent water changes are made.

Wong - Malaysia. Yes.

Jordan - Canada. With pairs, the pH will go up slightly when water changes are done, otherwise no.

Schulze - England. Slightly.

Left to right: Wattley, Prof. Dr. Dr. Herbert R. Axelrod and Bernd Degen during a 1990 visit to New Jersey.

Do You Use Tap Water, Well Water, Spring Water, D.I. (Deionized) Water, or Reverse Osmosis Water?

Schmidt-Focke - Germany. Mixed water - tap water blended with Reverse Osmosis water.

Schulze - England. D.I. water, mixed with local tap water.

Jordan - Canada. Breeding pairs I use Reverse Osmosis plus tap water (also for adults). For fry and young - straight tap water. (*J.W. This is also my procedure*).

Au - USA. I use tap water directly.

Wong - Malaysia. Tap water aged at least a full day.

Feiller - USA. Depending on the ages of the fish - from pure Reverse Osmosis all the way to pure tap.

Chan - Singapore. I recommend water stored in storage tanks for at least one-two days, after being treated with peat.

Reeves - USA. I use only tap water in my filtration system.

Shirase - Japan. I use only tap water.

Long - Zimbabwe. Tap water, which I do not age - only adjust temperature.

Dollman - USA. Tap water for fry and young adults. Reverse Osmosis water for older adults and fry under one month of age.

Nakamura - Japan. I had used tap water and well water, but presently use Reverse Osmosis water.

Handley - New Zealand. Tap water. (*J.W. Don Handley was mixing tap water with rain water when I visited with him a few years ago*).

Gobel - Germany. Tap water, D.I. water and Reverse Osmosis water.

Left to right: Harold Beck, Eberhard Schulze, the author, and Lo Wing Yat.

Successful discus breeders must be very careful of their water. To this end a myriad of water purification techniques have been developed. This is a typical view of what a modern discus-breeding facility might look like!

A nicely colored, healthy discus from the Gan Aquarium Fish Farm in Singapore. Except for a slightly undeveloped dorsal, this is a very fine fish.

Singapore Reds from the stock of Lim Boon. Photo by Don Standley.

Ken Reeves' Dwarf Turquoise discus.

Do you ever mix different types of water, and if so, when, and how much?

Schmidt-Focke - Germany. I prepare my tap water with the best grade of filter carbon and high moor peat, and mix it half and half with Reverse Osmosis water in a tank and get water about 6.0 pH - 6.5 pH, micromhos 70-80.

Wong - Malaysia. No.

Jordan - Canada. Fry and young I use tap water. Pairs and adults I use Reverse Osmosis plus tap water.

Gobel - Germany. 80 percent Reverse Osmosis water. 15 percent D.I. water. 5 percent tap water.

Handley - New Zealand. Occasionally, 50 percent rain water, 50 percent tap water. This is for my red Heckel discus only.

Nakamura - Japan. I now use Reverse Osmosis water, adding 20-30 percent well water. This water is for both growth and breeding. Well water is used after aeration only.

Dollman - USA. No.

Long - Zimbabwe. During our dry season when dam levels drop, ppm can rise to 100. I sometimes mix 50/50 tap and distilled water which is aged for 24 hours before use. It is also aerated well, and the pH and temperature adjusted if necessary.

Shirase - Japan. I have never mixed different types of water for my discus.

Schulze - England. Yes, I mix D.I. water with tap water to get micromhos of 80 to 120.

Reeves - USA. I hatch discus eggs which are to be raised artificially in a gallon jar containing 50 percent tap water and 50 percent distilled water. This appears to increase fertility 25-30 percent, but I have raised many fry from eggs hatched in routine system water.

Feiller - USA. For the eggs and fry up to two weeks of age no more than 15 percent tap water. From 2-3 weeks the transition from Reverse Osmosis water to eventually pure tap water by the time the fry are three weeks old. The growth tanks are pure tap water. Breeders are once again in a mixture of 85 percent Reverse Osmosis and 15 percent tap water.

Chan - Singapore. I use tap water. Few people in Singapore use well water, spring water, or any specially treated water such as Reverse Osmosis water.

Au - USA. No.

Frequency of water changes and what percent for pairs, adults, young fry?

Schmidt-Focke - Germany. Each day I change one fourth to one fifth of the water.

Chan - Singapore. I try to change 50 percent of the water every one to two days. Although feeding good quality food is important, I think daily water changes of up to 50-60 percent as being more important in encouraging rapid growth. I would like to relate an incident which has since made me a firm believer in daily water changes. A friend of mine had five Oscars in a 50-gallon tank. He fed them live goldfish, and changed the water once every fortnight (two weeks). After several months his Oscars hadn't grown well, and he sold them to another party who fed them the same amount of food or less! But he made one change, in that he change 50 percent of the water each day - and within two months the Oscars had more than doubled in size. Water change is the key to faster growth.

Au - USA. I change half of the water for adults and breeders every three days. For the fry and young fish, I change ten to twenty percent of the water every day.

Schulze - England. Daily twenty percent for breeders, and adults. For young discus I change two to twenty percent daily. Fry, two to ten percent daily.

Feiller - USA. Fry eating egg yolk get six water changes daily. Fry on *Artemia* for the first four days get four complete changes daily. Once moved to ten-gallon tanks at two weeks of age they receive at least one complete change per day. (50 percent morning and evening). For fry from three weeks to eight weeks, the tanks are cleaned and topped off every day with a 30-50 percent change every other day, depending on the condition of the tank water. Grow out tanks every other day 50 percent. Adults 40 percent every three days. They are not at all crowded, allowing ten gallons per fish.

Wong - Malaysia. Change of one third to two thirds daily for pairs and adults (depending on condition of the incoming water). For young and fry we change the water three times daily. One half in morning, one third at noon time, and one half again in the evening.

Reeves - USA. I utilize a central filtration system, so my water changes on any one tank effect the entire system. I routinely syphon all the fry tanks daily and 50 percent of the adults tanks daily, resulting in a ten percent water change. Twice weekly I backwash my filter and probably change 25 percent of the water on those days.

Shirase - Japan. For pairs I change one fourth of the water two to three times weekly. For adults I change 50 percent weekly. Young

Mr. Gan's Turquoise discus...and very nice they are! Photo supplied by Gans Aquarium Fish Farm, Singapore.

Discus spawning on a piece of PVC (polyvinylchloride) tubing.

discus, each day about 70 percent, and for fry I change about 80 to 100 percent daily.

Handley - New Zealand. One fourth change twice weekly for all discus.

Gobel - Germany. For pairs, adults and fry we change ten percent every 24 hours. For young discus we change thirty percent each 24 hours.

Nakamura - Japan. For breeding pairs change water 30 to 50 percent once in three day period. For the adult fish change water once each two to five days (this differs depending upon tank size, filtration, and number of fish in tank). For fry change water twice per day, and for young fish, once per day, amount being in one half to two thirds.

Dollman - USA. Breeding pairs change twenty percent daily. Adults change twenty five percent weekly. Young and young adults change ten percent daily. Fry change fifty percent daily.

Jordan - Canada. For pairs and adults change 33 percent on a 1000 gallon system every four days. For fry, change 75 percent each day.

Long - Zimbabwe. Adult discus, 30 percent daily. Young discus, 20 percent after each feeding. Pairs with fry, 50 percent daily. Fry raised in pans, every few hours.

Water temperature for pairs, adults, young, fry.

Schmidt-Focke - Germany. All the same. 28° to 29°C.

Dollman - USA. 84° to 86°F.

Handley - New Zealand. 80°F in winter, 85°F summer for all discus.

Nakamura - Japan. For pairs, 28° to 29°C. For fry, 30°C and for young fish 32°C. But for adult discus I adjust it between 27° to 30°C depending upon the situation.

Gobel - Germany. For pairs, adults and fry, 28° to 29°C. For young discus, 30°C.

Long - Zimbabwe. 30°C for all fish.

Shirase - Japan. Pairs, 28° to 30°C. Adults, 29° to 31°C. Young 30° to 32°C. Fry 30° to 33°C.

Reeves - USA. I try to maintain 82° to 84°F in my system - for all my discus fish.

Wong - Malaysia. Pairs, adults, young 82°F. For fry, 86° to 90°F.

Feiller - USA. Water temperature is a nightmare! Ideally, every tank in the fish room would be at 84° to 86°F. But because the room is heated the temperature ranges from 82° to 88°F. The tanks eight inches off of the floor of course are the colder ones, while all of the breeding tanks at six and one half feet are at 88°F. (*J.W. I have*

the same problem but strong fans help).

Jordan - Canada. All discus at 86°F (30°C).

Schulze - England. For pairs and adults, 85°F. For young and fry, 90°F.

Au - USA. Adults and breeders are kept at 80° to 82°F. Young and fry kept at 84° to 86°F.

Chan - Singapore. Dr. Clifford Chan did not inform me as to the temperatures in his tanks.

Temperature:

When you know—		To find—
Celsius (°C)	multiply by 1.8, add 32	Fahrenheit (°F)
Fahrenheit (°F)	subtract 32, multiply by 0.555	Celsius (°C)

Do you vary the water temperature, and if so, when and how much?

Schmidt-Focke - Germany. No.

Long - Zimbabwe. No, it has never seemed necessary.

Au - USA. Small drops in water temperature seem to induce spawning activities. When changing water for breeders I tend to put in lower temperature water to effect a few degrees drop. The heaters in the tanks will raise the temperature back to normal within half a day.

Schulze - England. No.

Feiller - USA. I don't have to vary the water temperature to produce results. Although I've had discus spawn within hours of being dumped into water four degrees F colder or warmer than what they came out of, I don't make a practice of it. I would like to be able to pin point an exact stimulus for breeding, such as lowering or raising the temperature two degrees or so, or altering the pH a full point - but discus will just not make it that easy for me!

Jordan - Canada. Pairs occasionally, with cold water changes to induce spawning, but for adults and young, never.

Wong - Malaysia. No.

Dollman - USA. No.

Nakamura - Japan. When medicating for *Spironucleus* I

This discus shows the difference between Asian and European standards. The color turquoise is very nice...but the conformation of the body is not satisfactory at all. Discus should be round...like a diskus that gets thrown...that is where the name came from in the first place.

raise water temperature to 36°C. And when I stop the spawning of a pair I raise the temperature to 33°C.

Handley - New Zealand. No - not important.

Shirase - Japan. Only if discus are sick I will raise water temperature.

Gobel - Germany. No.

Reeves - USA. My system is heated by a mechanically controlled valve on a hot water tank plumbed into the system. This results in a water temperature variation based on system pressure and unintentionally varies from 80° to 88°F.

Dirk Schlingmann of Dortmund and the author.

If necessary, how do you control chlorine or chloramines in your water?

Schmidt-Focke - Germany. My water, coming from the nearby Taunus Mountains, has very little chlorine in it, so I do nothing to control it.

Au - USA. I use anti-chlorine chemicals as directed by the maker. However, even with more than half of the tank filled with fresh tap water, the amount of chlorine in my tanks is almost not measurable and does not cause a problem for my discus.

Gobel - Germany. It's not necessary.

Reeves - USA. I have 2 ppm free chlorine in my tap water and make no attempt to eliminate it when doing water changes.

Shirase - Japan. Regarding chlorine, I use Sodium Thiosulfate.

Chan - Singapore. Add various commerically available anti-chlorines to the tank water.

Handley - New Zealand. With my water conditions, not necessary.

Jordan - Canada. Our municipal water system is quite good. However, I still use a standard "water conditioner".

Dollman - USA. Chlorine is added to my water, but the Reverse Osmosis and distiller remove it. In cases where I use tap water,

water changes are small enough that I do not worry about the chlorine added to the water.

Feiller - USA. I did not remove the chlorine from the tap water and found it to be an excellent prophylactic. Fish were seldom sick when I was able to follow this practice. I don't think parasites such as gill flukes could tolerate a 30 percent water change with chlorine in the water. My discus never showed any signs of stress from the treatment. Now, chloramines are a different story. But if you do try this method do so with caution and very gradually. I'm always concerned about telling some things about my discus, because what works for me may not work for you. There are few things that are black and white.

Wong - Malaysia. Hypo (Sodium Thiosulfate) is added either directly to the fish tanks or to the storage tanks. Zeolite is sometimes put in bags in the storage tanks.

Schulze - England. Water conditioners plus filtration over activated carbon.

Long - Zimbabwe. Chlorine in our water is very low, so I do not bother with conditioners.

Nakamura - Japan. For tap water, I use Sodium Thiosulfate. For Reverse Osmosis water I do nothing.

The author with Dr. Eduard Schmidt-Focke.

A pair of green turquoise discus during their spawning. The female is the upper fish. The male is cleansing the eggs which were laid on a PVC pipe. Photo by Richard Feiller.

A very healthy green turquoise discus bred on the Gan Aquarium Fish Farm in Singapore. This is a very robust fish.

LIGHT

How much light and for what duration?

Schmidt-Focke - Germany. For the breeders, only daylight.

Feiller - USA. The brighter the better. I keep the lights on for 18 hours per day. I have fluorescents everywhere. All have cool white bulbs, which are great for the plants and the algae, that I encourage to grow - while being inexpensive to purchase. My young discus love the green water. They color up almost as if they have been hormoned, and they grow faster than when in clear water. It takes a lot of light to be able to maintain algae growths like I have with the water changes I make.

Nakamura - Japan. I presently use one 40-watt fluorescent lamp per two 200-litre tanks. The lights are put on at nine a.m., and off at about nine p.m. I find that if the lighting is too bright the fish do not calm down.

Schulze - England. Ten hours per 24 hour day.

Dollman - USA. Four foot shoplights, available at any hardware store, with one cool white and one full spectrum bulb, hung four inches over large tanks, on for about 14 hours daily.

Shirase - Japan. The duration of light is from 7 a.m. to 9 p.m., with the brightness being 10 watts for each 60 cm of tank length.

Wong - Malaysia. Artificial lighting only until it is light enough outside.

Gobel - Germany. 15 watts per 50-gallon tank - on 14 hours a day.

Jordan - Canada. Lights are on 24 hours each day.

Long - Zimbabwe. I depend on normal daylight, but at night I use room lights for all tanks. All lights are out between 10 - 11 p.m.

Au - USA. Discus prefer natural daylight. I try to set up my fish rooms to provide the discus with at least 3 to 4 hours of indirect sunlight each day.

Reeves - USA. My fish room is lit with overhead fluorescent fixtures containing full spectrum tubes. The lighting is on 24 hours daily and is never varied.

Handley - New Zealand. 65 - 75 percent daylight overhead only. (*J.W. With Don Handley's skylight over his fish room he gets fantastic plant growth in all his tanks. With his continued success in breeding Heckel discus, plus Cardinal Tetras and many, many other hard to raise tropicals, Don is probably the "high priest" of tropical fish breeders*).

Is light varied at times?

Schmidt-Focke - Germany. No.

Reeves - USA. I use no individual tank lights. The tanks on the upper tier have moderately intense lighting and the lower tanks are quite dim.

Long - Zimbabwe. No.

Handley - New Zealand. Natural winter to summer lighting from overhead skylight.

Gobel - Germany. No.

Au - USA. Rooms are lit at least 14 hours a day either by indirect sunlight or a relatively dim fluorescent fixture.

Wong - Malaysia. No.

Shirase - Japan. No changes in the lighting at any time.

Jordan - Canada. No.

Dollman - USA. Yes, lights are left on for 24 hours per day when fry are feeding off the parents' sides.

Otherwise, no.

Schulze - England. No.

Nakamura - Japan. Lights not varied.

Chan - Singapore. No.

Feiller - USA. I don't vary the lighting, but I do keep a two foot fluorescent fixture above the ten gallon tanks on all night. I found that it has almost totally eliminated the nightime "wipe outs" of young discus that eat newly hatched brine shrimp. I don't agree that it is the salt in the shrimp that kills the fry, but the fact that they go to sleep with full stomachs. There was a point when I was losing as many as 50 percent of the fry during the night after turning out the lights. But recently while visiting Jack Wattley he enlightened (a little play on words) me as to his discovery re night lighting. Thanks, Jack! (*J.W. I can't really take credit for the night lighting "discovery", in that Brian Toomey in England, who is a friend of Eberhard Schulze, put me on to it*).

This is the certificate issued in Japan for authentic Wattley discus. Many fish may look like Wattley discus, but they do not breed true in most cases.

This high fin discus is more popular in Asia than in the USA and Europe. The crown of the head is misshapen, as is the eye socket, aside from which this is a nice fish. Produced by Gan Aquarium Fish Farm in Singapore.

Do you use reflection lights over your tanks?

Schmidt-Focke - Germany. Only for young discus - not for breeders.

Chan - Singapore. On some tanks, yes.

Jordan - Canada. No.

Dollman - USA. No.

Nakamura - Japan. I don't use reflectors.

Schulze - England. Yes.

Wong - Malaysia. No.

Handley - New Zealand. No.

Au - USA. No.

Shirase - Japan. I do not use any kind of reflectors on my tanks.

Gobel - Germany. Yes.

Feiller - USA. I use mostly shop lights - 4 ft. 2-40 watt tubes.

Reeves - USA. No.

Long - Zimbabwe. Yes, for parents with spawn or fry on sides.

Don Handley, 76 Park Road, Titirangi, Auckland 7, New Zealand.

FILTRATION

What kind of filtration do you use for breeders, adults, young, and fry?

Schmidt-Focke - Germany. Small power filters in each tank.

Long - Zimbabwe. Sponge filters.

Reeves - USA. I use a central filtration system consisting of a 400 gallon sump containing reserve water, a 3/4 horsepower high volume water pump, a swimming pool sand filter backed by a spa cartridge filter.

Shirase - Japan. For breeding pairs I use outside upper filters. For adults, young and fry I use same outside filters, plus sponge filtration.

Gobel - Germany. For all discus, biological filters and chemical nitrate filters.

Feiller - USA. In all my tanks I use sponge filters. I will occasionally run a diatom filter on a tank to "polish" the water.

Wong - Malaysia. No filtration is necessary because of the regular and large water changes. Occasionally, overhead filters are used in fry tanks if water is changed but twice daily.

Schulze - England. Trickle and internal sponge filters.

Au - USA. I only use sponge filters and corner box filters. Adults and breeders get both, but the fry get only the sponge filters.

Handley - New Zealand. Occasional sponge filters in fry tanks.

Chan - Singapore. Most people here do not use filters at all. The more enterprising design their own biological filtration systems, but generally filtration is not as elaborate as those used by Americans or Europeans. I use both sponge and power filters, although I do not believe too much in filters, as it makes one lazy to change water regularly. Frequent water changes precludes the need for any form of filtration.

Nakamura - Japan. For breeders, sponge filters in combination with small power filters, or wet-dry filtration. For adults, wet-dry. For young, wet-dry. For fry, sponges.

Jordan - Canada. I have two 1000 gallon systems, one for pairs and adults, the other for wild discus fish.

Dollman - USA. For the breeders I use sponge filters in combination with small power filters or wet-dry filtration. For adults, wet-dry filtration. Young, wet-dry, and for fry I use sponge filters.

What kind of filter medium do you use?

Schmidt-Focke - Germany. Dacron type material in the power filters.

Nakamura - Japan. The filter medium used is dacron wool.

Dollman - USA. Lava rock in my wet-dry filters. Sponges and commercial filter pads in my power filters.

Jordan - Canada. Both systems I use trickle filtration, using a seven-foot bioball tower. For young and fry I use a 280 gallon trickle system using gravel trays (consists of 28 ten gallon tanks). For the fry I use your (Wattley) method of raising them in bowls.

Handley - New Zealand. Nil.

Gobel - Germany. In the biological filters, broken basalt stones. In the nitrate filters I use exchange resins (MP 500 A Bayer).

Schulze - England. Mainly bio trickle and sponges.

Chan - Singapore. Sponges, at times.

Shirase - Japan. I use only dacron wool matting in the filters.

Au - USA. For ease of maintenance, I use only filter wool (dacron) in my box filters.

Reeves - USA. My filter media is a course sand with a second stage filter pleated cartridge. A portion of my water is run through a trickle filter containing dental appliance castings made of acrylic plastic.

Wong - Malaysia. We use dacron wool.

Feiller - USA. Most of my sponge filters utilize 3/4 inch pvc pipe with upholstery foam cut to size as the medium. On some tanks I use regular commercial sponge filters.

Long - Zimbabwe. Nil.

Dr. Kenneth Reeves, DVM, 8085 Owens Way, Arvada, Colorado 80005, USA.

A nice turquoise from Gan Aquarium Fish Farm in Singapore. The main defect is the misshapen forehead which seems to connect the eyes with a sort of saddle.

Are wet/dry trickle filters used in any of your tanks?

Schmidt-Focke - Germany. No trickle filters in my tanks.

Long - Zimbabwe - No.

Gobel - Germany. All my biological filters are dry trickle filters.

Handley - New Zealand. No.

Au - USA. No.

Chan - Singapore. I have not seen anyone in Singapore use wet/dry trickle filters.

Schulze - England. Yes, I use trickle filters in my tanks.

Shirase - Japan. I am not using any of those filters.

Dollman - USA. Yes.

Nakamura - Japan. I always use semi-dry filters of Japanese make.

Jordan - Canada. Yes.

Reeves - USA. A portion of my water is run through a trickle system.

Feiller - USA. I have on my 30 gallon fry (3 to 9 week old fry) tanks a central wet/dry system (trickle).

Wong - Malaysia. No.

What filter litre/gallon capacity per hour?

Schmidt-Focke - Germany. A power motor filter of 3000 litre capacity.

Wong - Malaysia. With our large water changes, power filters not too important.

Reeves - USA. Water flow to reach tank is individually controlled via the system valves. Fry tanks have 3 to 5 water changes per hour, while breeding pairs have only one water change per hour.

Long - Zimbabwe. N/A.

Dollman - USA. 300 gallons per hour.

Nakamura - Japan. Filter capacity is 60 litres per hour.

Jordan - Canada. All systems are turned over four to ten times an hour.

Feiller - USA. It provides for a three times turnover per hour. This does create a lot of turbulance for the fry, but their growth rate tells me that it benefits them.

Schulze - England. In litres, approx. 200 litres per hour.

Au - USA. Very slow water current through box filters or sponge filters.

Handley - New Zealand. Nil.

Gobel - Germany. Filter capacity is about 100 percent of tank capacity per hour.

Shirase - Japan. In the upper filters, 11 litres per minute.

Your opinion of peat in your tanks?

Schmidt-Focke - Germany. All peat is different, and I use high-moor peat (German Flora Torf) but not in the tanks. Only in holding tank, to prepare my water. (*J.W. Although I do not use peat in my hatchery, I have experimented with many different types of peat and found the German "Flora Torf" to be the best.*)

Gobel - Germany. Peat, if good quality, is very good, but you cannot use it together with exchange resin nitrate filters.

Shirase - Japan. I use peat only when I want to change the water quality to induce spawning.

Chan - Singapore. I recommend peat in storage tanks for conditioning water. A friend of mine puts a packet of peat (about a fistful) to treat 50 gallons of water, until it has a brownish tinge to it. It has worked well for him.

Au - USA. I don't use peat in my tanks.

Handley - New Zealand. Used occasionally in my Heckel discus tanks only.

Jordan - Canada. All my pre-filter tanks contain peat moss layers.

Nakamura - Japan Peat can be recommended where the water hardness is very high.

Akimitsu Shirase, Hirose Tropicals,8-48 Yatsu 4 Chome, Narashino, Chiba 275, Japan.

Top, facing page: Ken Reeves' aquarium setup for discus breeding in Colorado. Below, facing page: Mixed brown discus and blues at a young age. Nothing very special here.

Schulze - England. No.

Long - Zimbabwe. No, I do not use peat in my discus tanks.

Feiller - USA. I believe in theory that peat is probably beneficial. However, I do not use it for the following reason: The inconsistent quality. One bag will produce a pH of 5 and the next bag may even raise the pH, even though the manufacturer claims no additives. Also, I use Reverse Osmosis and carbon to strip the water. There is no need for either the softening or the acidifying qualities of peat.

Wong - Malaysia. Not necessary, as the water is very soft.

Dollman - USA. I have never tried peat in my tanks.

Reeves - USA. I have used peat moss in tanks previously and been favorably impressed. I do not use peat in my system now due to the volume which would be required and the trouble in maintaining an additional filter system.

Left to right: Manfred Göbel, Jack Wattley and Dr. Eduard Schmidt-Focke.

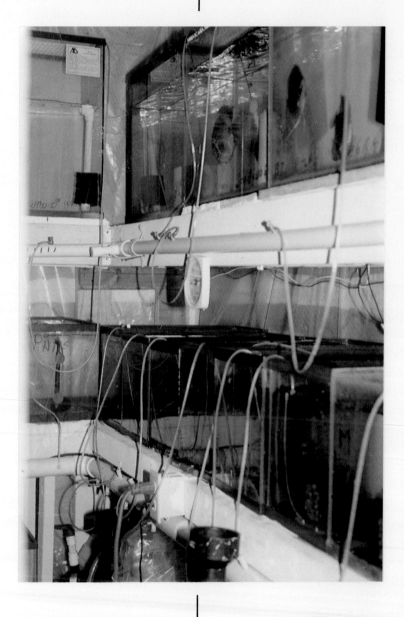

Richard Feiller's discus room in San Jose, California.

AQUARIUMS

What size of tanks do you use for breeders, adults, young, fry?

Schmidt-Focke - Germany. I have 100 litres for breeders - larger tanks of 200 to 300 litres for my other discus.

Shirase - Japan. For breeding pairs 60 cm wide, 45 cm deep, 40 cm high. For adult and young fish 120 cm wide, 45 cm deep, 40 cm high. For fry 60 cm wide, 30 cm deep, 36 cm high.

Reeves - USA. My system contains 20 gallon long, 30 gallon long, 40 gallon breeder, and 55 gallon tanks. Fry are raised in the 20 gallon tanks, breeders are housed in 30 gallon tanks, and grow-out is done in the 40 or 55 gallon tanks.

Wong - Malaysia. Breeders are in tanks of 30 inches by 20 inches by 28 inches. Adults are in tanks of 36 inches to 48 inches long, and fry are in tanks of 36 inches by 24 inches by 26 inches.

Dollman - USA. For breeders, 29 gallon tanks, but have used as large as 100 gallons. For adults, 50 to 90 gallons. Young, 50 gallons, and for fry, 10 to 20 gallons.

Schulze - England. Breeders 30x20x20 inches. Adults and young 70x20x20 inches. Fry 20x20x20.

Nakamura - Japan. For breeding pairs I generally use tanks of 120 litres. For discus other than the breeders I use tanks of various sizes.

Long - Zimbabwe. For breeders, 30 gallons. For young, 65 gallons. For fry, 5 to 6 gallons.

Feiller - USA. Sizes are: breeders, 20 to 26 gallons. Adults, 55 gallons or larger (for rest or pairing off), grow-out tanks are 35 gallons and larger. Fry 3 weeks to 9 weeks, I use 30 gallon, and for younger fry, 10 gallon tanks.

Handley - New Zealand. All adults, 6 feet long, 22 inches wide, and 16 inches high. All young discus in tanks of 4 feet long, 22 inches wide, and 16 inches high. All tanks with young discus are heavily planted. (*J.W. Fantastic plant growth in Handley's tanks,*)

Jordan - Canada. Pairs, 18 inches x 18 inches x 18 inches (25 gallons. Adults, six discus for 50 gallons. Juvenile discus, ten 3 inch fish for 50 gallons. Babies, 10 to 30 gallon tanks.

Chan - Singapore. Breeders in 20 gallon tanks, preferably two feet in length and about 16 to 18 inches in height. Adults, give at least 5 to 6 gallons per fish. This is often not possible because of the number of fish I have. I usually squeeze up to 15 fish for a tank of surface area of 6 square feet. I like to keep fish in the same tank from young to adult size. I overcrowd only if the fish are less than 2 cm in size.

The shape and size of this fish is exceptional, but the color is normal. In terms of the American-European discus trade this is an acceptable but not exceptional fish. Photo courtesy of Gan Aquarium Fish Farm, Singapore.

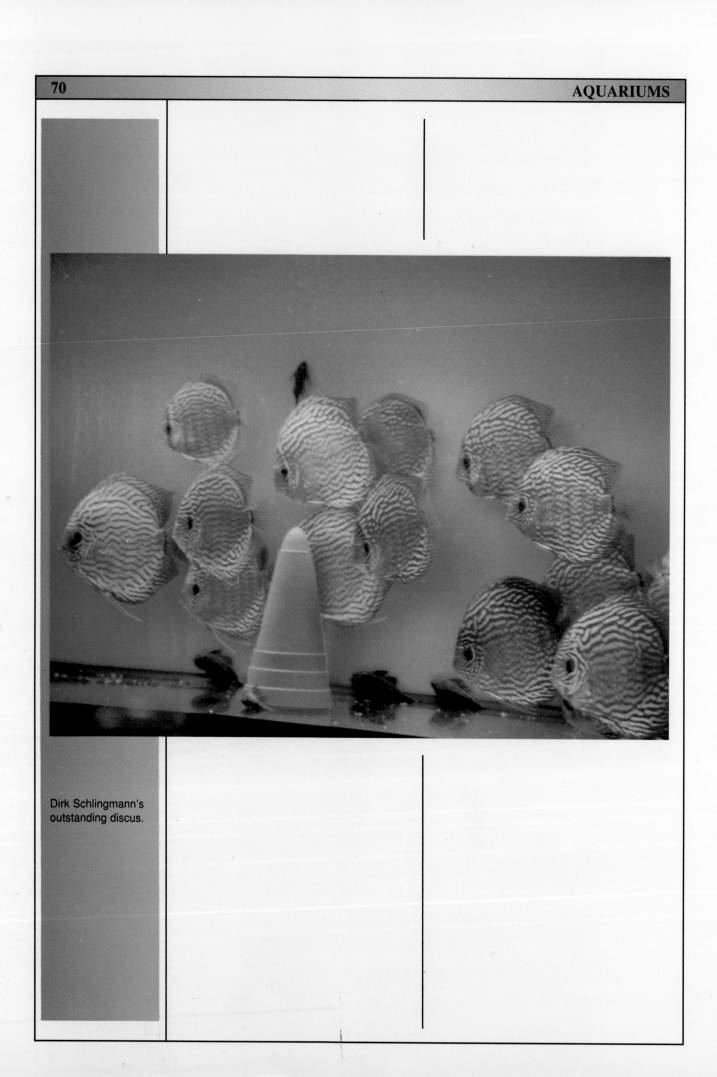

Dirk Schlingmann's outstanding discus.

Gobel - Germany. Breeders and fry with breeders, 50 gallons. Adults and young 100 gallons.

Au - USA. Breeders, 30 gallons. Fry, from 20 to 55 gallon tanks, as they mature.

1" = 2.54 cm

At what height from floor are most of your tanks positioned?

Schmidt-Focke - Germany. One meter or more.

Nakamura - Japan. More than one meter from floor.

Au - USA. Breeder tanks are placed at least five feet above ground level. In general, discus prefer tanks placed at high levels. (*J.W. I agree with Dick Au, although I have seen tanks of breeder discus in Bangkok and in Bad Vibel, Germany on the floor of the fish room.*)

Gobel - Germany. About 1.40 meters from floor.

Jordan - Canada. For pairs, never below three and one half feet from floor. For young and fry, never below two feet from floor. I truly believe that height is extremely important and will dictate growth and spawning behavior. (*J.W. Back to Dick Au again - he has a friend in San Francisco who has an aquarium shop with pairs of breeding discus. The tanks are placed as high to the ceiling as possible, and one must climb a ladder to see the pairs properly. Here in Fort Lauderdale, I use 55 gallon tanks for adult discus to pair off in. I just now measured the height from the floor - 18 inches. If I don't get new pairs out of those tanks after the first spawning they will continue to spawn in them.*)

Dicklam Au, 55 Riverton Drive, San Francisco, California 94132, USA.

Chan - Singapore. Tanks should be at least two feet from the ground to prevent jittery, shy fish from jumping, etc.

Handley - New Zealand. Planted tanks, four feet six inches to base. The larger, bare tanks are two feet, six inches to the base.

Wong - Malaysia. At least one foot from the floor - usually double decked.

Dollman - USA. Two to four feet from floor.

Feiller - USA. I have really cramped fish rooms. The first level of tanks starts at 8 inches of the floor, second level is about 42 inches, and the top level (for breeders) is 78 inches to the bottom of the tanks.

Shirase - Japan. Within 40 cm to 150 cm height from floor.

Long - Zimbabwe. Four feet from floor.

Reeves - USA. I have a three tier stand for fry tanks at 2 to 4 feet high. Breeders and grow-out tanks are 6 feet above the floor.

Schulze - England. My tanks to be at eye level.

Are your breeder tanks apart from the general room activity?

Schmidt-Focke - Germany. Yes. Breeders in upper room, young discus and fry in lower room.

Handley - New Zealand. No.

Schulze - England. No.

Reeves - USA. My breeder tanks are on the high portion of the stand and no attempt is made to isolate them from the general fish room activity.

Long - Zimbabwe. No, all fish are in same room.

Shirase - Japan. Yes. Breeder tanks are apart from the general room activity, and in a special warm room only for the breeders.

Dollman - USA. Yes.

Wong - Malaysia. Our bottom tanks are for young and fry, upper tanks for breeders.

Feiller - USA. Breeders are not at all sheltered from any activities, and people are amazed by the calm, unfrightened nature of my pairs.

Jordan - Canada. No.

Gobel - Germany. Yes, but only one tank (about 500 gallons) in my living room.

Au - USA. No. It is better for the discus to be accustomed to room activities and being observed.

Nakamura - Japan. Yes. Breeders are apart from the general room activity.

Chan - Singapore. No. All are in same general area.

Are any of your tanks planted with live plants?

Schmidt-Focke - Germany. Yes. I have *Ceratopteris* (floating form) in tanks, as well as *Philodendron gigantea* (for removing nitrate from tank water).

Au - USA. No, I prefer to use bare tanks.

Long - Zimbabwe. No live plants in my tanks.

Nakamura - Japan. Some tanks do have live plants.

Gobel - Germany. Yes, but only one tank (about 500 gallons) in my living room. (*J.W. This 500 gallon tank that Manfred Gobel has in his living room is truly a show piece - with extra-large size discus spawning amongst beautiful plants. I wish I had something like it.*)

Chan - Singapore. No. Most of us keep discus by themselves. Usually no plants at all.

Shirase - Singapore. No tanks with live plants.

Reeves - USA. I love planted community tanks, but I have no planted tanks in my system.

Schulze - England. Yes, in one large show tank.

Handley - New Zealand. Yes, in all my top level tanks. (*J.W. In some of Don Handley's tanks the plants outnumber the discus!*)

Chong Mok with the 1000 gallon fiberglass storage tanks he uses for processing discus water.

Wong - Malaysia. No plants in our discus tanks.

Jordan - Canada. No.

Dollman - USA. Yes. Water Wisteria, Amazon swords, and *Aponogeton crispus*. (*J.W. When David Dollman successfully spawned his Heckel discus it was in a well planted tank.*)

Feiller - USA. I love live plants. I think they are a real benefit to the fish, and in turn the fish are a benefit to the plants. I have Amazon sword plants with leaves as much as 24 inches long. I keep algae suspended in as many tanks as possible. In those tanks that do not get sufficient light to support a good algae growth I allow water sprite (*Ceratopteris*) to grow. It is amazing the difference in water quality between tanks that have live plants and those that don't. All plants that require gravel to root in are potted in plastic pots, or in ceramic pots.

Stephen Long and his wife.

Do you keep any other genera of fish with your discus? If so, what kind?

Schmidt-Focke - Germany. No other fish with the discus.

Handley - New Zealand. Yes. Cardinal tetras, Topline tetras, and occasionally I keep New Guinea and Australian Rainbows with my discus.

Schulze - England. Only in show tanks, where I keep Cardinal Tetras.

Feiller - USA. I keep no other fish with my discus.

Shirase - Japan. At one time I kept Angel Fish, small type Tetras, and *Corydoras* with the discus, but not now.

Gobel - Germany. Yes, *Ancistrus* catfish. And in my show-tank I keep *Pterophyllum altum*.

Chan - Singapore. Keep discus by themselves.

Nakamura - Japan. Occasionally I keep *Apistogramma* and small size Characidae with discus.

Dollman - USA. No.

Wong - Malaysia. Yes, we keep algae eaters (catfish) with the discus.

Au - USA. No other fish with the discus.

Long - Zimbabwe. No.

Reeves - USA. I have kept dwarf Cichlids, Rainbows, Tetras, *Corydoras*, Uarus, Gouramis, and *Plecostomus* with my discus. I now keep several species of *Corydoras* and five species of *Plecostomus* in my system to ease the tank maintenance.

Jordan - Canada. No other fish with the discus.

Dale Jordan,
71 Melon Lea Cover,
Winnipeg, Manitoba
Canada R2G 2L4

A nice Asian-quality fish bred by Gan Aquarium Fish Farm, Singapore. The high body type is sought after in Asia but is not well liked in Europe or America.

BREEDING

Do you raise your discus fry in a natural way or by artificial means?

Schmidt-Focke - Germany. I raise now only naturally. In the past I have been successful with a mixture of egg powder mixed with powder of flower pollen.

Reeves - USA. I routinely raise fry artificially, but usually I do have several pairs with fry on their backs.

Wong - Malaysia. We raise all our discus naturally.

Chan - Singapore. Artificial raising of discus fry is not practiced in Singapore.

Dollman - USA. I raise the fry both naturally and artificially. (*J.W. In my hatchery I raise about one third of the fry naturally, the other two thirds artificially.*)

Long - Zimbabwe. Both ways.

Nakamura - Japan. Although I generally raise the fry in a natural way, occasionally I do raise them artificially.

Jordan - Canada. 75 percent artificial - 25 percent natural (*J.W. About like me*).

Au - USA. Both

Gobel - Germany. Only in a natural way.

Schulze - England. Natural way.

Feiller - USA. I artificially raise the majority of the fry. Occasionally I do allow the parents to raise them, but it is impractical from a commercial standpoint. My experience with pairs that I allow to carry their fry is that they become unpredictable as breeders. They may spawn while carrying fry and then either the new fry or the existing fry get eaten. Or they may spawn a week or so after the fry are removed, or maybe not for six months. I have found pairs to be excellent parents for a spawn or two and then eat the next several spawns before resuming parental care. Also, by raising the fry artificially, I eliminate the risk of the parents starting out with 250 fry and then destroying over half of them. I have one pair in particular that if they start out with 75 fry they will end up with about 70 fry. But if they start out with 300 fry they will still only raise about 70 fry! I know from experience that the other 230 fry were not deformed.

Handley - New Zealand. In a natural way.

Shirase - Japan. Now I raise discus in a natural way.

(J.W. A German discus breeder, Bernd Degen, states in his book "Discus-How to Breed Them," that German discus are among the best in the world. I do agree. I do want to point out at this time that there are many well known and many not so well known American discus breeders, as well as others from most parts of the world, who are

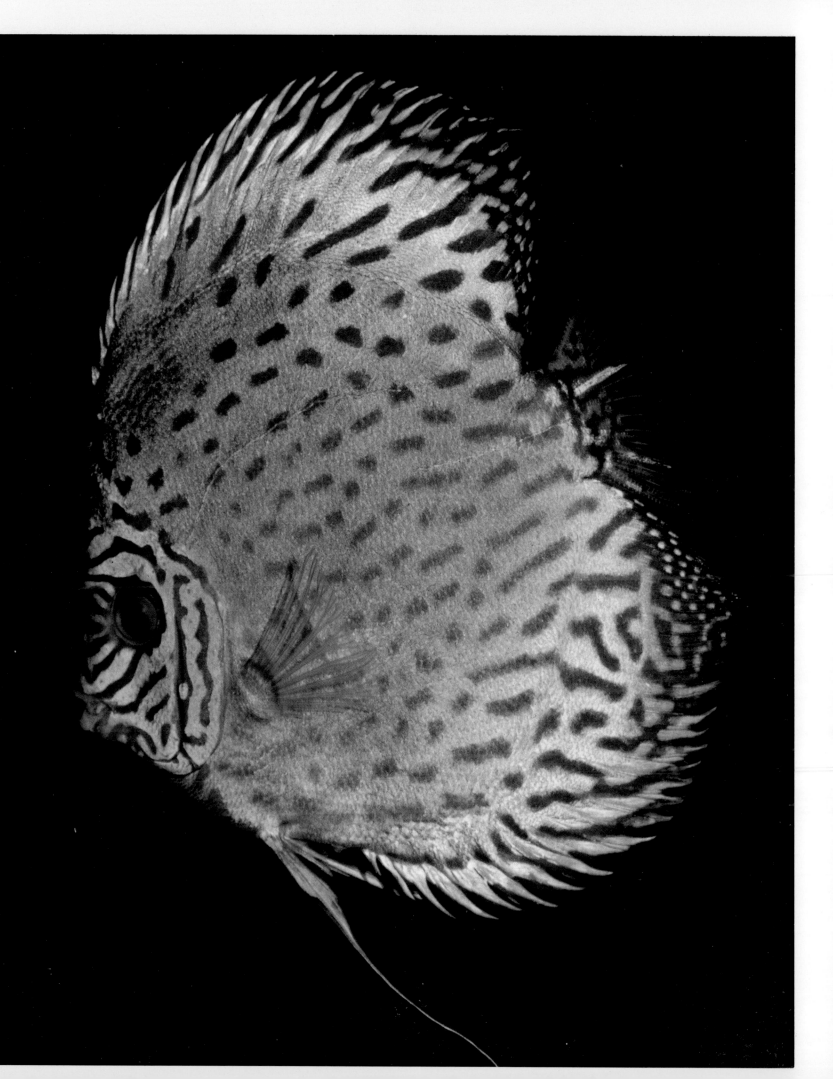

producing discus of the same high quality and are seriously dedicated to their work with discus. It is of interest that of the three pure strains of discus that have made the most impact in the tropical fish market in the past 20 years (Schmidt-Focke reds, Mack Galbreath powder blues, and my turquoise strain), two of these three strains were developed here in the U.S.A.

I want to refute his statement as to the use of "colored gravel, skulls, divers, etc.", by American aquarists. Not so. While this may be the case with some beginners, it is demeaning for him to say so, as we have many serious and knowledgeable discus keepers in America. What with my many trips to Germany, visiting with the various discus keepers there, I can assure him that we have as many advanced breeders here.

He further states that I use large amounts of Methylene blue for my artificial hatching of the discus eggs. Again, not so. In fact, most breeders here in the USA who artificially raise discus use much more Methylene blue than I do. It would be interesting to know his source of information, as I have never discussed any of my discus breeding procedures with him. For the record, I use twelve drops of 1% Methylene blue in 2 gallons of water.

His statement that I enjoy only partial success in raising discus fry by artificial means and that their growth rate is poor is not true. I generally raise approximately 40% of the fry with the parents, the other 60% artificially, and I can assure him that I can achieve better growth rate with my artificial method. Generally, the guy who criticizes the artificial method of raising discus fry is the same guy who has never had any success in doing so.

I use no dehydrated, bakers egg yolk at this time. It's not always easy to obtain, and I find I can do as well using a hardboiled yolk mixed with a raw yolk. Mix the two together and freeze the mix. The raw yolk is important for its viscosity sticking power on the sides of the sloping pan the fry will be in. OK, your frozen egg yolk mix is in your freezer, and you are now waiting for the discus fry to rise up and swim around the top of the pan water line. You've already removed them from the Methylene blue water 6 to 8 hours before hatching, putting them into clear water while they are still on their spawning site. You have light air in middle of pan. Whey they all rise up from the bottom of the pan - but not before - drop the water level down enough so the top 2 inches or so of the pan is completely dry. I use a paper towel for this. Are you still with me? You've already defrosted the yolks and you are now adding one part newly hatched Artemia to 4 parts egg yolk. Crush the Artemia into the yolks, mixing it all in together. Take your middle finger and very carefully put or smear the mix around the top of the pan. Approximately 1/2 inch wide is OK. Let it dry there for 15 minutes or so, then carefully bring the water level back up, covering all the mix.

If you have a vigorous spawn, they will attack the food almost immediately. You will have very light air in center of pan. I use only an air line - no air stone, and you will have added an antibiotic to inhibit bacterial growth in the water. I use a combination of Nitrofurazone and Furazolidone,

This fish has excellent color but very poor body shape. Photo supplied by Gan Aquarium Fish Farm, Singapore.

which is readily available in aquarium shops, adding 25 mg. to one gallon of water. At this point you should be able to go six hours or more before your water change. At this point drop the water level down as low as possible, with the fry in the pan of course, and fill up again with new, fresh conditioned water - same pH. Be careful not to knock the fry around too much in adding the new water. Continue this procedure for 12 to 14 hours, maintaining your correct level of antibiotic at all times. At the end of the 12 to 14 hour feeding program you will syphon out all egg mix water, carefully wiping all egg from the sides of the pan. The fry will then settle down for the night in nice clean water.

Some discus fry accept newly hatched Artemia *the first day of feeding, but I prefer to feed the egg -* Artemia *mix for at least two days, after which time I introduce the newly hatched* Artemia *on the third day, along with the egg mix. By the fourth day all fry should be accepting the* Artemia. *And it's just as easy as it looks here!)*

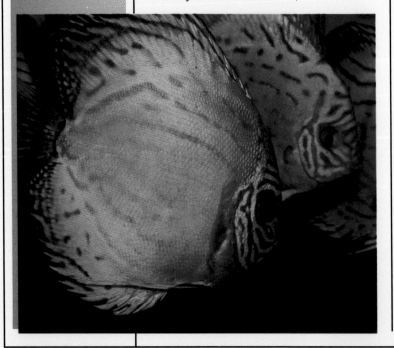

C.W.Wong's discus.

If raised naturally, at what age do you generally remove the fry from the parents?

Schmidt-Focke - Germany. Usually in about two weeks - depending on size of the fry.

Long - Zimbabwe. Three to four weeks in most cases.

Shirase - Japan. I remove the fry from the parents at about two weeks.

Gobel - Germany. Three to four weeks.

Handley - New Zealand. Variable, depending on stock situation. Can vary from two weeks to six weeks.

Feiller - USA. When fry are raised with the parents I normally keep the fry with the parents for three weeks.

Schulze - England. Two to three weeks (*J.W. For me, ten days to two weeks.*)

Au - USA. I prefer to leave the fry with the parents for a minimum of one week, and possibly up to three weeks dependent on the compatibility of the pair.

Dollman - USA. One week.

Nakamura - Japan. Fry are removed from parents ten days after hatching.

Chan - Singapore. Separate them after one week of free swimming.

Reeves - USA. I separate the fry from their parents at two weeks.

Wong - Malaysia. Between seven to ten days.

Jordan - Canada. Seven days - *Artemia* is added on the third day. I feel something should be said at this point about artificially raised discus. I have raised all my present pairs artificially. Each pair, when needed, will raise their young naturally. The aspect of artificially raised parents not being good parents is ludicrous. (*J.W. I agree*).

With fry mortality highest after removal from parents, what steps do you take to remedy this?

Schmidt-Focke - Germany. I put the young discus at first in mixed water of the breeder tank with water of the new tank (for the young discus), and I add Trypoflavin in the water. (*J.W. Trypoflavin in USA is Acriflavin*).

Wong - Malaysia. Raising the temperature of the water in the fry tank, more frequent water changes, and regular feedings.

Reeves - USA. I have no problem with mortality after removing fry from parents. Water quality is maintained, even with heavy feedings, by three to five hourly water changes. Additionally, I keep an *Ancistrus* catfish in fry tanks to keep tanks clean. Also, the fry tanks are syphoned daily.

Gobel - Germany. After removal of fry from parents normally none will die. No problem.

Shirase - Japan. I don't experience fry mortality.

Jordan - Canada. Never really had a problem with pre-mature fry mortality.

Chan - Singapore. Keep them in clean water at temperature of 32°C.

Nakamura - Japan. Check water quality and change water as needed.

Dollman - USA. I haven't had much problem with fry mortality.

Au - USA. Start the fry with a smaller tank such as five or ten gallon, depending on the size of the spawn. Use water directly from the parents' tank. Use a seeded sponge filter and make sure that the water temperature is slightly higher. Make certain that water quality in the tank stays good by making daily water changes and syphoning out debris on the bottom of the tank.

Schulze - England. Usually no fry mortality.

Long - Zimbabwe. I try to leave the fry with the parents as long as possible. I have also found it helps to delay feeding *Artemia* to the fry as long as possible after hatching. I feel that discus fry fed live *Artemia* are subject to *Oodinium* disease (velvet), so I monitor the *Artemia* feedings very carefully.

Feiller - USA. The reason that I keep the fry with the parents for such a long time is that I find they do not make the transition to *Artemia* as readily as do fry raised on the egg yolk formula, even though I start supplementing their diet with *Artemia* at one week of age.

Handley - New Zealand. Never experienced this problem.

What spawning medium do you use (PVC, flower pots, plants, bricks, etc.)?

Schmidt-Focke - Germany. Flower pots.

Nakamura - Japan. Mainly I use PVC, but at times I use bricks or flower pots.

Handley - New Zealand. Plants and flower pots.

Feiller - USA. I prefer that the breeders spawn on the four inch diameter by eight inch long PVC pipe. (*J.W. This what I have always used. I like PVC because it has much less porosity than pots, cones, bricks, etc., therefore less chance to house bacteria.*)

Chan - Singapore. Did not answer this question.

Jordan - Canada. I use a tupperware dry spaghetti holder filled with gravel. (*J.W. This sounds very interesting to me*).

Long - Zimbabwe. Driftwood and PVC although my discus have a remarkable ability to avoid these, and spawn on the tank glass.

Reeves - USA. I use a PVC sleeve on my tank overflow system. The eggs are laid on the PVC which is removed and replaced with a duplicate, following the spawning.

Schulze - England. I use flower pots.

Au - USA. Yellow fire bricks or black slate strips.

Shirase - Japan. Flower pots only.

Wong - Malaysia. Bricks. Often nothing - the pairs spawn on tank bottom or tank sides. (*J.W. If one has an "egg eating" pair of discus that spawn on the glass the eggs can be carefully removed with a new single edge razor blade. With care, you can successfully capture 70 percent or so of the eggs - to hatch and raise artificially.*)

Dollman - USA. I usually use slate or PVC pipe, but I have used driftwood at times. (*J.W. David Dollman's Heckel discus spawned on driftwood*).

Gobel - Germany. PVC.

What steps do you take to induce spawning?

Schmidt-Focke - Germany. Feeding pairs with live foods. The best being live mosquito larvae.

Dollman - USA. I introduce a pair to a 29 gallon tank with a small power filter and a sponge filter. I then proceed with heavy feedings and heavy water changes - five gallons daily.

Gobel - Germany. Introducing male and female discus into the breeding tank. Nothing more.

Wong - Malaysia. One resort is to add a seasoned adult discus (one that has bred before) to the tank of the new pair. (*J.W. This has worked for me at times.*)

Feiller - USA. To induce spawning I have no secret formula or method. I do not use hormones. I have tried everything from drastic water changes to pH changes to singing to them. And there is no one thing that I can count on to produce on demand results.

These discus were raised by David Dollman, 205 North State Street, Marengo, Illinois 60152, USA.

Shirase - Japan. By putting another adult discus in the tank.

Handley - New Zealand. Water changes.

Au - USA. Change about half of the tank water and drop the temperature by a few degrees F.

Nakamura - Japan. Mainly by changing water, but occasionally I put in another male or female discus. Also, at times I will make temperature changes.

Schulze - England. Big water changes.

Long - Zimbabwe. I use several possibilities: separate the pair, increase water changes, divide the tank with clear glass and place third fish next door, lower (then raise) water temperature, lower the pH to 6.8.

Jordan - Canada. Cold water changes and live food.

Reeves - USA. To induce spawning I reduce tank temperature to 78-80°F for several weeks. While the tank temperature is low I reduce feedings to once daily. After several weeks, I gradually increase water temperature and begin the daily feedings. After two weeks of normal temperature I may do a 50 percent water change if spawning hasn't begun. With fish that still refuse to spawn I try to change social structure by moving fish, introducing new fish which I already know to be an aggressive spawner.

How far in advance do you take these steps?

Schmidt-Focke - Germany. Usually about two weeks.

Long - Zimbabwe. I have never used any set pattern.

Reeves - USA. Several weeks as a rule.

Nakamura - Japan. It differs depending on time and circumstances, but generally within a week or so.

Schulze - England. Two to five days.

Handley - New Zealand. Only my normal two weekly water changes.

Jordan - Canada. Cold water changes will usually induce spawning one to three days later. However, if fish are on a spawning cycle no inducement is needed.

Shirase - Japan. About one week before the expected spawning.

Wong - Malaysia. Once the pair show signs of courtship.

Chan - Singapore. Generally about a week to ten days.

Feiller - USA. How far in advance do I take these steps? 52 weeks a year. The bottom line to breeding discus is simply three things: clean water, a good diet, warmth.

Sounds simple, doesn't it? If I slack off on these three things the productivity goes down.

Dollman - USA. Approximately 3 to 4 weeks before spawning would normally occur.

Gobel - Germany. No steps taken.

Au - USA. Sometimes breaking apart the pair of discus for a few weeks and reuniting them helps.

The author visiting Shirase and his famous discus installation in Japan.

DISEASE

What disease do you encounter most frequently?

Schmidt-Focke - Germany. Most frequently - "Hole in the head" disease.

Gobel - Germany. Gill worms.

Au - USA. Gill flukes, *Capillaria*, and "angelfish disease."

Reeves - USA. I am a veterinarian and receive many calls regarding fish health. This gives me an opportunity to evaluate many discus hobbyist problems along with observing problems in my own fish room. I do autopsies on many discus, my own and fish from stores and from hobbyists. I routinely sacrifice a few fish of my own each month to monitor any diseases in my system. I generally select fry which are not thriving, assuming these will be sentinels of any disease problems. The disease problems I see most frequently are *Hexamita* and gill flukes. I also have seen *Capillaria*, tapeworms, dietary problems, bacterial infections, and the plague (which I believe is increasing in frequency again).

Long - Zimbabwe. What is known as the plague which effects discus fish.

Dollman - USA. Gill flukes.

Handley - New Zealand. Rarely any in recent years. (*J.W. When I visited Don Handley several years ago, I saw no diseased discus in his tanks, nor in discus tanks of other breeders in the Auckland area. The N.Z. government has imposed strict laws regarding the importation of tropical fish and there is virtually no chance of quantities of junk discus reaching the aquarium shops there.*

Wong - Malaysia. Diseases caused by protozoa, as well as stress, and bacterial disease, and viral infections.

Schulze - England. With my own discus, I encounter no major problems, but with imported discus the discus disease (slimy bodies).

Feiller - USA. Pollution in the fry tanks from overfeeding. I was having a problem with gill flukes until Flubenol came my way.

Shirase - Japan. Gill disease.

Jordan - Canada. Never really have problems if water conditions are good. However, minor bacterial problems due to injury, and the discus plague have been experienced.

Nakamura - Japan. The disease I most encounter is gill flukes. To a lesser extent I find *Spironucleus* (*Hexamita*), and *Flexibacter columunaris*.

What medications do you use most often, and for what diseases do you use them?

Schmidt-Focke - Germany. Since I change water daily (one forth) and have a complete circulation through my tank filters, I have no problems with disease. All the different diseases are very much reduced.

Feiller - USA. For problems with the fry I use a combination of Nitrofurazone/Furazolidone.

Wong - Malaysia. For bacterial infection, Gentamycin in combination with Formalin/ Potassium. Potassium Permanganate $KMnO_4$ is used with Formalin most often for almost all types of diseases. If a case of bacterial rot should appear we use Gentamycin sulphate. Very few discus breeders in Malaysia use Gentamycin because of the high cost. They usually use Tetracycline.

Nakamura - Japan. For gill flukes I use Formalin. For *Spironucleus* I use Metronidazole, and for *Flexibactor columnaris* I use Tetracycline or Nitrofurazone. For serious infestation of gill worms I use Masoten (Dylox).

Jordan - Canada. For the discus plague I use Gentamycin. For general bacterial diseases I use Erythromycin.

Shirase - Japan. Formalin, for the gill disease.

Schulze - England. Chloromycetin and Metronidazol for slimy body discus plague.

Long - Zimbabwe. Furazolidone for the discus plague, with coarse salt.

Handley - New Zealand. As advice to other discus breeders in N.Z., for gill flukes I suggest Formalin 3 drops per gallon for 8 hours followed by total water change. For *Hexamita* I suggest 1200 mg. Metronidazole per 50 gallons, three treatments, a day apart, plus 95°F.

Dollman - USA. Formalin for the treatment of gill worms (flukes).

Reeves - USA. The treatment I use and recommend most frequently is water change. 90 percent of disease in discus is related to stress, and poor water quality is the most frequent stress. If you begin experiencing a disease problem with any fish go first to your water test kit, not to your drug cabinet. Many times a tank cleaning and water change will cure your fish with no additional treatment. (*J.W. If you think you know all the answers about discus - but want to pick up one bit of advice, then make it this one from Ken Reeves*).

Gobel - Germany. Flubenol. 5 percent for gill worms (flukes).

Au - USA. Unless I can clearly identify the disease, I would attempt to cure the problem by massive and frequent water changes as well as raising water

Craig Barrel of Hartford, Connecticut produced this amazingly colorful female from a *Symphysodon discus discus* **X** *Symphysodon aequifasciatus haraldi.*

temperature to over 90 degrees F for four to five consecutive days. I use a few drops per gallon of Formalin solution (37 percent) for gill flukes or any external parasites. Furazone green (Nitrofurazone, Furazolidine, and Methylene blue) for any bacterial or fungal infections.
Metronidazole for *Hexamita*.

What dosages do you use and in what time frame to effect a cure?

Au - USA. Because of the concentration differences, I recommend following the instructions from the chemical makers.

Gobel - Germany. 250 mg Flubenol for each 100 litres of water on day one, day seven, and day fourteen. Use only Flubenol without DMSO or Acetone. After 21 days change 50% water.

Shirase - Japan. Put one cc of Formalin in ten litres of water. Change water after three hours. Take same procedure after three days, and again three days later. (three treatments).

Wong - Malaysia. Formalin, 3 drops per gallon for three days.

Nakamura - Japan. Formalin, 4 cc in 100 litres of water for 7 hours, and add some quantity during the last hour of treatment. Repeat treatment 3 times (four days apart). Tetracycline, let fish bathe for one week. Metronidazole, one mg. per litre of water, raising the water temperature to 35.5°C. treatment to last 3 days.

Dollman - USA. One drop of Formalin per gallon for three days.

Reeves - USA. The medications I use most frequently are Metronidazole, Formalin, and salt. Clean water and these medications will control almost all discus disease problems. *Hexamita (Spironucleus)* is a protozoal infection of the intestinal tract. If the disease is neglected it can become extremely harmful and effect many other organs in the fish. *Hexamita* thrives in low oxygen conditions and elevated temperatures. These are the conditions we stimulate when intensively feeding a crowded tank of fish. *Hexamita* is the most frequently observed problem in a discus tank. The symptoms of *Hexamita* are dark fish with clamped fins. Infected fish may have white, stringy feces, and are often observed approaching food and then backing away without eating. In adult fish *Hexamita* are often secondary invaders of fish parasitized by *Capillaria* or gill flukes. *Hexamita* is treated with Metronidazole, which can be used as a bath at 25 mg per gallon, or orally by mixing at 250 mg per ounce of paste food. It is often best to medicate the water initially, then when the fish are eating more readily to switch to medicated food for an additional 5 days. All treatments should be accompanied by daily water changes.

Dactylogyrus is an egg laying fluke which parasitizes the gills of discus. In a closed environment such as an aquarium the infestation can become severe in a short period of time. Symptoms of gill flukes are dark colored fish, often hiding in tank corners and refusing food. The fish demonstrate rapid respiration and stay near the surface or near the outlets of the aquarium filters. The treatment I favor is a combination of 37% Formaldehyde and salt. I use one tablespoon of salt per 5 gallons of tank water accompanied by two drops per gallon of the Formaldehyde. Observe the fish for signs of stress and be prepared to do an immediate water change. Usually no stress is noted, but at 8 to 12 hours I do a 50% water change. The adult and larval flukes are killed with this treatment, but the eggs are not effected. To eliminate the disease repeat treatment once a week for 4 treatments. *Capillaria* are treated like nematode intestinal parasites. These parasites are common in wild caught discus but may infect any discus or angelfish. Infected fish show weight loss and often have stringy, white feces. To identify the parasites you must find the eggs in the feces or do a post-mortem and find the parasite in the intestine, spreading it out under the microscope, where, if *Capillaria* are present, they can easily be seen. If this is not done the *Capillaria* will not be seen, as they are on the inside - not outer side- of the intestine). The least stressful treatment for *Capillaria* is Mebendazole, a veterinary worming medication. Mebendazole is marketed as Telmintic and is available through veterinarians. I prepare a paste food containing 100 mg of Mebendazole in 8 oz. of beef heart. Feed the medicated food for three consecutive days and repeat treatment after seven days.

(*J.W. These dosages from the respondents are all precise and exact. When it is necessary to medicate, don't do as many do, and estimate. Be precise. After all, you don't go around estimating the time of day, do you? The new Untergasser book on Discus Diseases is your best guide*).

Do you feel that pH has an effect upon the efficiency of the medication?

Gobel - Germany. For medication, pH should be between 6.0 and 6.7.

Jordan - Canada. Yes. The lower the pH and hardness the more effective the treatment.

Schulze - England. Yes.

Dr. Ken Reeves' Red Turquoise discus spawning on a piece of PVC pipe.

Feiller - USA. To my understanding all medication is effected by pH and buffers in the water. That is why I cringe when someone gives an exact dosage, without asking what kind of water it is being administered in.

Handley - New Zealand. Extremes either up or down in pH reduce the effectiveness of the medication being used.

Reeves - USA. I use most discus medications orally so aquarium pH does not effect the medication. Some antibiotics are effected by pH so medicated baths should be done at a neutral pH (7.0).

Nakamura - Japan. pH is a very important factor. Too high or too low a pH will often affect the effect of the medication.

Au - USA. Lower pH seems to help recovery of most fungal and bacterial infections.

Wong - Malaysia. Yes.

Shirase - Japan. When medication is used a pH of 6.0 to 7.0 is best.

Dollman - USA. Not too important unless pH readings are very high or low.

Long - Zimbabwe. Yes. A range of pH 6.2 to 6.7 is best for nearly all medications.

What treatment do you consider best for *Spironucleus, Capillaria, Flukes?*

Gobel - Germany. *Spironucleus* (*Hexamita*). Day one, Metronidazole 700 mg in 100 litres water, and raise temperature to 33°C. Day four, temperature down to 30°C. Day nine, Metronidazole 700 mg in 100 litres of water, temperature again at 33°C. Day twelve, temperature down to 29°C. and change 30% of water. For *Capillaria* and flukes, Flubenol 5% over 21 days.

Shirase - Japan. For *Spironucleus* I raise water temperature to 35-36°C and I then treat with Metronidazole.

Wong - Malaysia. For *Spironucleus* we treat with Metronidazole.

Au - USA. For flukes I treat using Formalin.

Nakamura - Japan. Metronidazole for *Spironucleus*. Formalin for flukes, and for *Capillaria* I use Caombantrin or Tetracycline.

Jordan - Canada. For *Spironucleus*, Metronidazole and heat. For both flukes and *Capillaria* I treat with Flubenol and DMSO. (*J.W. Dimethylsulfoxid, known as DMSO*).

Schulze - England. For *Spironucleus* I use Metronidazole.

Beautifully marked Gan discus with lips that are almost human!

Feiller - USA. For *Spironucleus* (*Hexamita*) I treat with Metronidzole. For both gill flukes and *Capillaria* I have had excellent results using Flubenol and DMWO administered to the water and maintained at a given level.

Reeves - USA. Three bacterial diseases that do occur in discus tanks are Piscine Tuberculosis, Septicemia, and *Columnaris* (*Flexibacter columnaris*). It is important to know them, although they do not occur as often in discus tanks as *Spironucleus*, *Capillaria*, or flukes. Piscine Tuberculosis - a chronic wasting disease, usually of older fish, affecting all organ systems. The fish exhibits emaciation, exophthalmus (popeye), dark coloration, lethargy, and often swelling of the abdomen associated with fluid accumulation (dropsy). Disease is produced by a bacteria, *Mycobacterium* sp. The organism is a gram positive, non-motile aerobic bacillus. There are several species of *Mycobacterium* which occur in fresh water fish. Diagnosis is made by finding nodules containing the organism in the liver, spleen, or kidney. Often severe degeneration of these organs is noted. Highest incidence is in discus from southeast Asia due to hygienic conditions under which they are raised. This is generally a chronic wasting disease of older discus. Prevent by maintaining tank hygiene and a high quality diet.

Septicemia. A generalized acute bacterial problem produced by *Aeromonas hydrophilia* or *Pseudomonas* sp. These are gram negative enteric bacteria and produce disease due to stress and crowding. Septicemia is indicated by acutely ill fish demonstrating abdominal swelling (dropsy), exophthalmus, and blotchy hemorrhages on the body and the fins. Also, Septicemia may complicate severe hexamitiasis. Infected fish should be isolated, maintained in very clean water and treated with Furanace at 0.2 ppm for 5 days.

Flexibacter columnaris is a gram negative rod-shaped bacteria which inhabits the aquatic environment. This bacteria will contaminate external wounds, such as mouth abrasions occuring due to spawning activities. These infected areas are indicated by white cotton-type lesions around the involved site. *Flexibacter* can also produce an acute fin rot resulting in necrosis of all fin tissue including the fin rays. This is not an enteric disease, so treatment can be administered with water-soluble antibiotics such as oxytetracycline, nitrafurazone, or triple sulfas. Potassium permanganate is also effectively used as a longer-term bath.

(*J.W. The time of hatching of Dactylogyrus gill fluke eggs varies greatly, depending on the species involved. For that reason we can really only guess as to which species is the culprit in the tank and what time frame to use regarding medication*).

Do you have any special techniques for saving otherwise doomed fish?

Feiller - USA. With doomed fish, which I assume you mean sunken bellies, dark holes in the head, white, gelatinous feces and not eating, or eating very little. That is what the freezer is for! There have been numerous times that I have tried to play the savior to the discus in this condition and there have been times when the treatments have been initially successful. But, in the majority of cases where they survived they were seldom useful as breeders and more often than not they remained stunted. If I am determined to resurrect an otherwise dead discus this is the course I take. First, I move it to a 10 to 20 gallon tank (bleached) that has been thoroughly rinsed. The tank is filled with pure Reverse Osmosis water, with vitamins added. I can then evaluate the levels in ppm of medication that I am using. Next I add 6 oz of rock salt (for 10 gal. tank) to offset the nitrites, because the tank filter will not be functioning as a biological filter. If a severe infestation of gill flukes is evident I will treat for the flukes first. For a temporary, quick treatment I will use a Formalin/Malachite Green compound. It relieves the problem long enough to medicate the other problems. You can also use straight Formulin - 3 drops per gallon. Without adequate oxygen in their blood the fish will not survive anyway and gill flukes rob their host of oxygen. Many times treating for gill flukes is enough to lighten their color and start them eating again.

I will have taken a feces sample at the beginning, before treatment of any kind. If the fish has *Hexamita* or *Capillaria* I will see evidence of it in the stools. If they have both I treat for the *Hexamita (Spironucleus)* first. Metronidazole is fast acting and has no apparent side effects. In three days the fish can be moved to completely new water and then rested for a day or two before being treated for *Capillaria*. For *Capillaria* I do prefer Flubenol 5% with DMWO left in the water for at least 21 days. This will eradicate the egg laying flukes and eliminate the *Capillaria*. I tried the method of injecting Levamisole (Tramisol) directly into the stomach with a pediatric stomach tube with very poor results. It is too traumatic for the fish. Because of the size of the tube, it only works on adult fish. Unfortunately, it is the young discus that succumb to most parasitic infestations the quickest, not the adults.

Another parasite that is common to discus that are fed black worms is the tape worm. I've dissected young discus whose stomachs and intestines were packed with the tape worms. Dronsit, a medication requiring a prescription, will take care of the problem. Here again the dosage will vary from 2 to 6 ppm depending on the hardness of the water. A good reason to use Reverse Osmosis water is that the Reverse Osmosis water requires less medication. If the fish is

Nicely colored high body type discus from the Gan Aquarium Fish Farm in Singapore.

Beautiful Asian discus with a body not as fully developed in height as many of Gan's beautiful discus. Photo supplied by Gan Aquarium Fish Farm, Singapore.

bloated because of the amount of parasites creating a blockage in the digestive tract I've had limited results in using Epsom salts (Magnesium Sulfate), one tablespoon per 5 gal. of water. It acts as a laxative. Also excellent for getting discus out of shock.

For hole in the head which I find two forms of, reduce any stress factors, make frequent water changes, and add an aquarium multivitamin high in the B complex and C and the problem should clear up in a few days. The form of hole in the head that produced pus will also respond to this treatment. I've never had it to fail for me, and I have used it on fish with large head craters. The form of hole in the head that produces these pustules does not always mean *Hexamita* is present. I have checked discus with these symptoms and was unable to find any of the parasites.

Jordan - Canada. If the treatment is not effective, the fish is destroyed.

Nakamura - Japan. I can't answer this question unless I know the cause.

Au - USA. If this discus has been ill for a relatively long time and looks emaciated it is better to discard the fish humanely. Water changes, plus high temperatures seem to work as a last resort (at times).

Wong - Malaysia. No special techniques for doomed discus.

Shirase - Japan. No special techniques.

Long - Zimbabwe. I'm going against the grain, but I have seen live Tubifex worms bring some doomed fish back to health.

Gobel - Germany. No.

Reeves - USA. Treating doomed fish is difficult unless you know the cause of the illness, which we rarely know. *(J.W. Same answer from Nakamura-san)*. I have found most thin discus, chronically ill, to have a combination of parasites. The fish may have *Capillaria* or gill flukes, often both, and these are almost always accompanied by a very heavy infestation with *Hexamita*. I feel that elevating the water temperature to 95 - 100°F to stimulate the fish's immune system and using Metronidazole in the water is the most likely treatment to work. Delay other treatments until the fish is eating and less stressed - then experiment with other parasite treatments.

Dollman - USA. If I do not know the cause I will not try to save the fish. (*J.W. I firmly believe we must have good management techniques for solving our discus problem; those techniques being (1) first relieve the symptoms, (2) then eliminate the cause, (3) prevent it from happening again.*)

MOST IMPORTANT FACTOR

If you consider one factor of discus cultivation to be of more importance than any other factor, what is that factor and why is it of more importance?

Schmidt-Focke - Germany. Water changing every day with clean water. Fresh, prepared water into each tank, being certain that tank bottoms are always clean.

Dollman - USA. I consider water quality to be of the utmost importance in the cultivation of the discus fish. I don't necessarily mean pH and/or hardness, but the amount of ammonia, nitrites, dissolved oxygen. None of the other factors really matter if you do not have good water quality. Without good water quality the fish will never be able to reach full potential.

Gobel - Germany. Quality of water and food. If the quality of the water and the food is ok, you don't need chemicals nor medicaments in most cases.

Long - Zimbabwe. Healthy water means healthy fish.

Au - USA. Clean water and diligent aquarium maintenance. Discus that are kept in a healthy environment seldom get sick. So - an ounce of prevention is better than a pound of cure.

Shirase - Japan. Watching the daily health condition of the discus, plus the quality best suitable for breeding the fish.

Won - Malaysia. Here I will consider only water quality and food, with water being of more importance. Through experience, if our water quality is not ideal our discus get sick and spawning is not successful. When water is ideal our fish remain healthy and spawnings are successful, regardless of what food is given the fish.

Handley - New Zealand. Water quality, because of the high quality of water in the discus' native habitat.

Feiller - USA. Not enought can be said for diet, clean water and warmth. But I consider the most important factor in the successful raising and breeding of discus to be a sixth sense not unlike a green thumb. If an individual does not sense when his fish are in need of something, when they are stressed or ailing, he could memorize every method of discus care known to man and yet never be successful in maintaining these beautiful animals. These fish are very demanding and you must have a passion to work with them.

Jordan - Canada. The factor I feel the most important in the cultivation of discus is the aspect of sticking with pure strains and working with the proper genetic pools, i.e. wild and true strains. The names and colour varieties given by many of today's discus breeders is truly an embarrassment. The idea of giving fish names of every color spectrum is absolutely ludicrous. In my opinion it takes many, many years to produce a pure strain of fish. It is all too often that every time you pick up a fish magazine a new super purple electric turquoise discus is being advertised. I feel very strongly about these breeders playing on the public's lack of available knowledge. It is my hope that this book, by Jack Wattley, will shed some light on this problem area.

(*J.W. Yes, there are too many so-called strains being produced and sold amongst discus breeders. To develop a true strain you most certainly should have a specific goal in mind when you make a cross. What are you trying to accomplish in making your cross? A more high fin discus, larger size, more color (perhaps with splashes?) or what? Today we are saddled with a batch of trash discus and junk crosses, most of which don't mean anything. Do you want to change the course of discus breeding in the world? You must know the background, or history of the stock you are working with. In other words, know where you are going. It was once said (not by me) that if you don't know where you're going, at least you're never lost.*)

Shirase Thunder Flash discus in a Shirase aquarium.

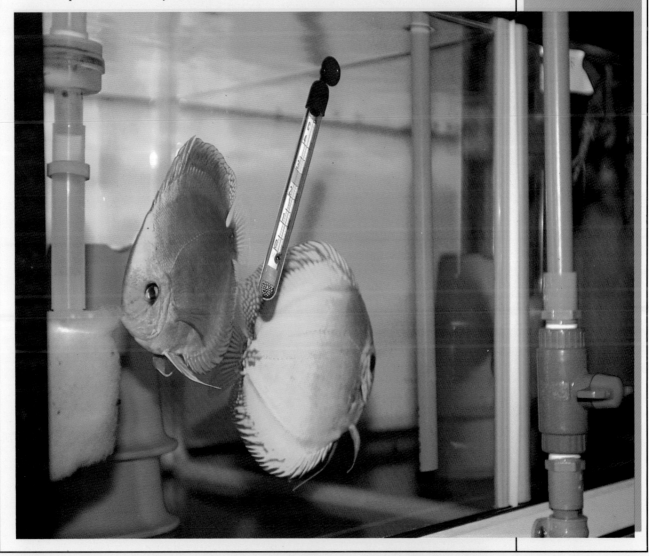

LONG RANGE FUTURE OF DISCUS HOBBY

What views do you have regarding the future of the discus hobby?

Schmidt-Focke - Germany. Not very good. Pesticides in waters. Many discus on the market have ekto and/or endo parasites. Mixtures of all the species. We must save the natural species of discus. (*J.W. None of us have the awareness of preserving and working with the discus species that the king, Dr. Schmidt-Focke has. Many times the two of us would visit the various discus importers in the greater Frankfurt area - with Schmidt-Focke always showing much more interest in the species rather than in the tank bred hybrids.*)

Shirase - Japan. With few exceptions, most discus keepers seem to be satisfied to simply keep and breed their fish with no thought regarding the improvement of the bloodlines. So now it is important to set apart the best breeders, and stabilize a good bloodline, thinking more regarding quality and not quantity. (*J.W. Excellent point*).

Schulze - England. The discus hobby is growing worldwide, as we all know. But we must show the hobbyist only the very best quality fish.

Gobel - Germany. As long as it is a challenge to keep and breed discus people attempt to do so.

Nakamura - Japan. My team (Hirose, Nakamura, Shirase and Suzuki) is presently working together to develop new color strains. We hope to stabilize color in our green discus. I think the discus hobby in future will be divided into two groups. One is to simply keep beautiful discus in planted aquariums to admire them, with no thought of breeding them. The other group will produce excellent quality discus (*J.W. For the first group to admire, no?*) by the improvement of the species. However, the latter group will need great perseverance, and at times difficulty. In addition to the above, the joy of researchers of the science of taxonomy and behavioristics of discus will follow.

Chan - Singapore. In future we all should attempt to cultivate live foods such as tubifex, blood worms, *Daphnia*, etc. in more sterile conditions. Also, we must develop methods to allow faster growth and earlier maturity of our discus, which will then allow more generations of fish to be produced over a shorter period of time.

Wong - Malaysia. Because of the huge production of discus by S. E. Asian breeders the prices will come within the means of all discus hobbyists. As an exporter of discus I have become more selective in my discus purchasing, which, in turn, will cause the breeders I purchase from to be more selective. And of course the discus hobbyist should certainly stay away from artificially colored discus, which unfortunately are being processed these days.

Handley - New Zealand. Because of overall poor water quality in the world, discus keeping will remain a bit difficult in spite of improved knowledge, plus the fact that it is difficult to obtain fresh stock from the wild. (*J.W. As we all know, due to the excessive mining in Amazonia, Mercury is appearing in the waters there. In what quantity, and in what areas? Harmful to the discus? I would say so!*)

Dollman - USA. I feel the discus hobby will continue to grow rapidly as more hobbyists begin to keep discus and to learn the fish is no more difficult to keep than most other aquarium fish. I feel we have almost reached the pinnacle as far as the turquoise strains go. I think it is entirely possible that someone will develop a strain of solid red discus within the next ten years. (*J.W. I'm glad you said ten years and not two years. If it is done - solid red discus - it will take ten years or so*). I would like to see the discus return to it's original round body shape. Lately I have seen many discus with a very inferior body shape. These fish should not continue to be procreated.

Long - Zimbabwe. Let us hope the discus hobby continues to grow.

However, it is a pity that so many breeders are out to make a fast buck, thereby causing the discus to lose the individuality they so much deserve.

Feiller - USA. I am concerned by the unscrupulous discus merchants who are doing a tremendous damage to the discus hobby. The names of strains proliferate the magazines, as do the fraudulent use of names such as Schmidt-Focke and Wattley for the purpose of merchandising. But as long as these fish bring a good price there are those who will continue to cross anything with anything, or sell whatever they have and call it whatever they need to in order to sell their fish. I have bought many different strains over the years and raised their progeny only to find out that they did not breed true, but were, in fact hybrid crosses of who knows what. On a positive note, I know there will always be good breeders who will continue to produce excellent discus, with new strains. And there will always be a market for discus. I believe we have just touched the tip of the iceberg in the color and fin development of discus. And what about colors - reds, lavenders, golds, greens, albinos? What about a miniature discus? Where twice as many could be kept in a smaller tank.

Jordan - Canada. Along with new publications, the hobbyist should start to obtain quality wild stock to continue the proper balance of hybrids and wild strains.

Really nicely colored Gan's Red Turquoise produced in Singapore.

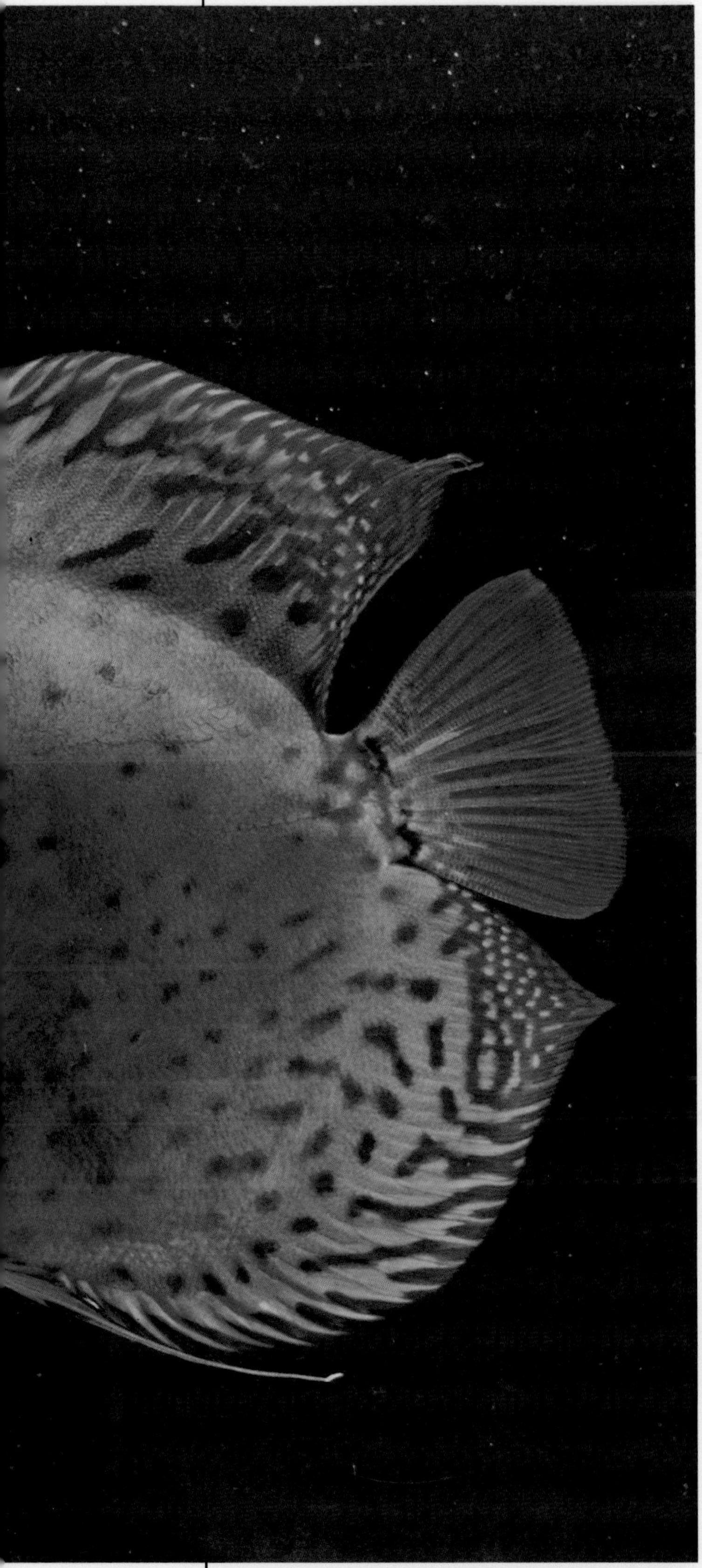

Au - USA. Currently, too many people breed discus only for financial rewards, turning out as many fish as possible and create as much commercial hype as possible. Average quality discus will become much more available and affordable, while premium quality ones will become practically impossible to locate.

One of the Shirase-type Thunder Flash discus from Japan.

NEW COLOR VARIETIES

Are you attempting to develop new color variations, and if so, what direction are you taking?

Schmidt-Focke - Germany. I made crosses with all the species, but not much progress. Only the different crosses of the solid green ones, which are developed in Germany, and now are all over the world. We must make line breeding if we want to save a good colored strain.

Au - USA. No. My effort is in the development of attractive striations, physical size, and good body conformation. I am also attempting to locate and maintain pure, wild stock such as the brown, green, and blue strains.

Handley - New Zealand. Attempting a red Heckel - Lake Tefe cross, which should result in robust, colourful discus.

Jordan - Canada. Yes, with Schmidt-Focke's new red-brown discus. In my opinion, one of the nicest strains that I continue to work with.

Nakamura - Japan. One attempt is to stabilize Turquoise discus with a more red colored body. And to stabilize and set a strain of green discus (those with red spots all over the body). Lastly, to develop Wattley Turquoise bloodline, but with Heckel discus black band, and I fear this will be the most difficult one to realize.

Feiller - USA. Yes, I am presently working on three different varieties. The first is for a solid lavender discus. I have two males that emerged from the fry of Jack Wattley's Coerulea Turquoise strain. (*J.W. I wouldn't call my Coeruleas a strain yet, as I really haven't fixed, or set it yet*). I'm also working on a deep metallic solid blue discus, and lastly, on a Heckel-Wattley cross. (*J.W. Richard, get together with Nakamura on that!*) I have always had a special place for the Heckel discus, and would love to see a solid Turquoise with the three solid Heckel bars.

I am working with fish in each of these categories. I have F_1 progeny from two of the three. It will be three generations before I'll have been able to sort out the progeny separating the hybrids from the strain. All of the traits that I am pursuing are recessive. The F_1 progeny are dominant hybrids, the F_2 progeny are 1/4 dominant, 1/2 dominant hybrids, and 1/4 recessive. The 1/4 recessive (if desirable and fertile) can be backcrossed with the P_1 to produce an F_3 generation with a 50% recessive, provided everything is kept in simple form.

Long - Zimbabwe. No, not at the present time.

Dollman - USA. Am now working on developing a tank bred population of Heckel discus that will spawn as readily as any other discus. Pure Heckel discus are

Shirase also produces well-marked uniform discus like these.

rarely spawned in captivity. I find this unfortunate because I see great potential in the Heckels for developing new color strains as well as reintroducing some wild blood into the aquarium strains. I have succeeded in obtaining fry from wild Heckels which I presently have.

Gobel - Germany. Yes, I continually select only the very best fry for future breeders, and make it a point not to inbreed any of my fish. This point is very important.

Wong - Malaysia. We are always attempting to improve the quality of our fish, for size, shape of fish, and of color.

Shirase - Japan. Developing a discus with blue face (not hormoned blue face), as well as a new discus with deep red color, which we hope to name it Red Thunder Discus. *(J.W. Dr. Axelrod recently discovered that this fish exists in nature in the Rio Jau. He calls it the "cabeça azul," which means "blue head" in Portuguese.)*

FINALLY

Any points in this questionnaire that you feel have not been covered?

Schmidt-Focke - Germany. Nearly all fish medications damage the organs very much, but by working with water changing and bringing the water, by circulation, back to the internal filter, I have no problems with discus sickness.

Feiller - USA. Yes. The artificially raising of the discus fry and the methods used. More hobbyists are interested now in raising discus fry away from the parents. (*J.W. Richard, as you can see, I've updated my procedure of raising discus fry artificially, although I still do raise many discus fry with the parents*).

Schulze - England. To show the discus hobbyist only the very best quality discus, and to have the poor quality in shape (mainly) and in colour disappear.

Handley - New Zealand. I believe I may have been the first person to successfully breed the Heckel discus, and from the original pair I kept the strain going for 12 years. In 1985, with the need for new blood I obtained a stock of wild Heckels, having gotten one pair to spawn, but with no fry. The Heckel is much more difficult to breed, much like the Cardinal Tetra, but I've had them successfully spawn in a large tank, planted, and with other fish as tankmates. (*J.W. I have seen Don Handley successfully spawn and raise the Cardinal Tetra - Paracheirodon axelrodi*).

Au - USA. Discus raising should be leisurely, enjoyable and uncomplicated. Lately, there has been too much emphasis in chemicals, filtration systems, etc., all of which would scare off the potential discus hobbyist. We should reemphasize the basics of aquarium maintenance and demonstrate that discus raising is not as difficult as it is made out to be.

Nakamura - Japan. I anticipate forming an international discus organization where we can exchange information regarding discus, and to cooperate with each other in order to promote and maintain the pure strains of discus fish throughout the world.

C.M.Wong's discus.

(J.W. What do discus hobbyists do with the excess fish they raise? They generally are sold to local aquarium and pet shops, as well as to other discus hobbyists. Many aquarium shops are very willing to trade equipment and supplies to discus hobbyists for their excess fish. Some successful discus hobbyists, initially selling fish to their local shops, become semi-commercial dealers when they produce more fry than the shops can handle. At that point they advertise in the various aquarium journals and aquarium society bulletins. One successful discus breeder I know, far from any large metropolitan area, had so much difficulty selling his fish in such an extremely limited market that he offered them to me for far less per fish than the price of a six-pack of 'cerveza'.

And what happens to any discus fry that are defective? Where do they end up? Unfortunately, many of them find their way into the tanks of unsuspecting, novice discus hobbyists. Many of the defects in young discus are caused by poor water conditions, but the inferior looking fry can eventually produce high quality young of their own. However, there's nothing aesthetically pleasing about a defective looking discus, whether the defect was due to poor water or to a hereditary factor, so in many cases it is probably best to humanely destroy the fish. If the defective problem has been proven to be due to poor water conditions the breeder should not continue producing more young discus until the problem has been resolved.

At what size are the majority of discus sold? Most discus are sold at 3cm to 5cm (1.5 inches to 2.0 inches). Many commercial discus breeders, especially in Asia, also sell discus in larger sizes. They are listed on price lists as Small, Small-Medium, Medium, Medium-Large, Large, and Extra Large. In some cases these size listings can be very deceptive, with a discus listed as a Large being no more than 10cm (4 inches) in size. A question often asked me is does the size of the fish include the tail or just the body. Everyone has their own opinion of this, mine being that we do not include the tail in determining the size, although the tail is part of the fish, no?

Tropical fish exhibition and aquarium shows. At aquarium society shows here in the USA discus do not usually play a big part. This is also the case in larger national aquarium symposiums. At the latest American Cichlid Convention I saw but 7 tanks of discus, all located in the back of the exhibition room, whereas there were many more tanks of other cichlids. Discus do not show up well in exhibition tanks. They are subject to much more trauma, in the move from their own tank to a new exhibition tank, which probably is too small for the discus, and will no doubt be completely bare. In nearly all cases the water chemistry will be different. At that same ACC convention I saw a number of red discus that had been flown in from Germany for the show. I was not at all impressed. Yet, when I saw them later in the year in the breeders tanks in Germany I was very impressed. Nevertheless, if you do plan to show your discus, at least give them the best shot at looking and acting their best. Bring along your own water. That's important! Bring tamper-proof aquarium heaters of the proper wattage. If the show rules permit, bring backing material. Your fish will show up better, and besides enhancing their colors, will also act as a calming device.

A subject that elicits much controversy is regarding the correct names of the various discus strains, and who is entitled to use them. Let's take Mack Galbreath's 'Powder Blue' discus strain. If Mr. Galbreath sells the F_1 young from this pure strain that he personally developed, does the buyer have the right to state that he has Mack Galbreath's 'Powder Blue' discus? Of course. If the buyer (whom we'll refer to as John Smith) in turn successfully breeds these F_1 discus, then what? At that point Smith is working with F_2 fry. He advertises these F_2 in the various aquarium trade journals. Does he refer to them as Mack Galbreath's 'Powder Blue' discus, John Smith's 'Powder Blue' discus, or simply as 'Powder Blue' discus? At this point let me say that there are many interpretations as to what is correct, or who is correct, and I don't think the subject has been properly addressed.

When Dr. Herbert Axelrod asked me to address the subject of possible jealousy among the many discus breeders, I said, "Herb, I could write a whole chapter about the petty jealousy that exists internationally amongst discus breeders. Jealousy is a human trait which unfortunately exists everywhere. If a discus breeder achieves a degree of prolonged success, he or she can be virtually certain he or she will be subject to being run down or 'shot down' by disgruntled competitors. The rumors together with their sources invariably find their way to the discus breeder. There is not much to be done about it as inevitably it will touch every successful breeder at one time or another. Objectivity will help to bring the situation into the right perspective.)

Britta Schmidt-Focke, on the left, with the author's daughter Pamela, in Wattley's fish room.

Water Purification With an Emphasis on Reverse Osmosis

by Richard Feiller

It is being proven over and over that the quality of our waters is degenerating at a very fast rate. There are an estimated 70,000 different chemicals in existence today with approximately 1000 new ones added each year.

To be successful breeding discus, we must have a basic understanding of the water quality needs of our pets. And we should attempt to provide for their needs. What water purification alternatives are available?

Water purification can mean a number of different things. However, it should take the following steps of progression. First start with a good particulate filter; normally 10" elements in a plastic housing. These elements are rated from 1 - 20 micron in rejection. The most commonly used is the 5 micron as a prefilter for either Reverse Osmosis or Deionization.

The next step would be to add GAC (Granular Activated Carbon, or a carbon block), depending on your water demands this could be anything from a cartridge for a 10" plastic housing to a large commercially prepared tank. This is all that is needed for many would-be breeders.

While on the subject of GAC another very important point has to be brought out. There are many types and grades of GAC. What you need to use is a coal-based GAC #40, preferably acid washed, with an iodine rating of at least 900. I am not going to go into all the characteristics of GAC other than to say that the Iodine rating, grid size and what it is derived from are critical. Coconut shell based GAC, commonly used in the electronics industry can alter the pH to as high as 9.5 from a pH of 7. This high pH has the ability to pass right through both DI resins and R/O membranes. And believe me the end result can be tragic.

The next step if the results are still not satisfactory is to add one of the following forms of water purification.

1. DISTILLATION – Needless to say distillation has come a long way since the lab. In fact, look to the future to see more and more multi-stage flash distillation, vertical tube distillation and vapor compression distillation. Two additional forms of distillation are by crystallization and for those of you living in a constantly sunny warm climate, solar humidification. These newer forms of distillation are fast and efficient with a minimum water loss. Many water companies are starting to use some of these methods.

2. ION EXCHANGE RESINS (cation & anion ion exchange and deionization) – Probably the best example of ion exchange resins is the water softener in your home. (This includes those cute little bags of resin found at tropical fish stores that are recharged with rock salt). This by itself is probably the least desirable method of softening water for your fish! It utilizes sodium ions for Calcium Carbonate ions. Yes, the water registers soft with reagents, but the Total Dissolved Salt (TDS) is still high. Potassium Chloride can be substituted for rock

salt, but instead of going to that expense while still maintaining a high TDS, why not just get the right equipment in the first place?

The proper type of ion exchange units incorporate both cation & anion resins. There are two different types of cation and anion DI units available. The first is a mixed resin bed unit, that is to say that it contains both cation and anion resins within the same housing. This type can not be recharged by the hobbyist, but must be turned back in to the supplier and changed for a recharged unit.

The second type is a system made up of two different tanks. One tank contains the cation and the second tank the anion resins. This is the type of DI unit most often purchased by the discus hobbyist and breeder. Each of these tanks can be isolated from the other and recharged with either acids or alkalis.

The deionization process is a two step process where the final product is hydrogen ions that dissipate into the air leaving the water deionized.

There are numerous types of ion resins out. Most of which are probably not the right resins for aquaculture. Too harsh a resin will strip the protective mucus off your fish and can even kill them.

This is not to say that DI is not for aquaculture, quite the opposite. Deionization with the proper resins is a relatively fast effective way to purify water. A small DI unit can produce purified water much faster than a small reverse osmosis unit can.

The brand of anion resins that I hear most commonly used in aquaculture are the MP500A by Bayer and Purolite A500P. There are strong base anions designed with organics in mind. The cation to use with A500P is c100. Units made up to handle these resins with the aquarist in mind are available through several sources in TFH magazine, including Feiller Fisheries.

The disadvantage to DI units is the use of harsh alkalis and acids that are necessary to recharge the resins. These chemicals are very hazardous not only to the users, but especially their children and pets. Not to mention the environment, even though both the alkalis and acids are supposed to be neutralized before being poured down the drain. The fact that they are pH neutralized does not eliminate them from concern.

Another disadvantage when used as the primary source for water purification is they have to be recharged frequently. Depending on the quality of the feed water, the small units can be spent after just a couple of hundred gallons of water. At this point they need to be recharged.

The normal use of DI resins in industry is as a water polisher after R/O and prior to the final polishing with an ultrafiltration membrane.

3. REVERSE OSMOSIS – Reverse osmosis is new in concept being in existence since around 1965.

In the United States, reverse osmosis is the safest and over the long haul the most economical means of softening water. What is reverse osmosis? To understand reverse osmosis, one must understand osmosis.

Osmosis is one of the basic methods of transferring liquids between cells in all living things. In nature there has to be a balance of pressure between adjoining cells of living tissue and between the living tissue and it's surrounding environment or the cells would explode or collapse.

Example #1: To duplicate this process let's take a bowl and in the center of this bowl place a semipermeable membrane (a type of material that an osmotic exchange can take place through). Now fill one half of the bowl with sea water, which is at least 35,000 parts per million of total dissolved solids, and in the other half of the bowl an equal amount of distilled water.

The side with sea water is rising and of course the half with distilled water is lowering by an equal amount. What you are witnessing is an osmotic exchange of liquids to stabilize the osmotic pressure. Sea water being much denser (if the TDS is 35,000, osmotic pressure is 398 psi) compared with 0 osmotic pressure of distilled water. These two liquids must stabilize at the same osmotic pressure. So the sea water is thinning itself down by drawing in the distilled water. Eventually the distilled water will be absorbed and a dehydration of the membrane will take place.

Example #2: Reverse osmosis is just the reverse of osmosis as the very name indicates. In example number two we will take the same quantities of sea water and fresh water with a semipermeable membrane in between them, but with a twist. We will use pressure on the sea water side to force pure water out of the sea water, until the remaining sea water is even denser (this is referred to as concentrate). Now the very opposite of the first example will take place. The sea water side will become lower as the

distilled water side rises.

GENERAL INFORMATION CONCERNING REVERSE OSMOSIS:

Reverse osmosis was designed for desalination, to do just what we did in example number two. However, reverse osmosis is used with many other liquids and products. Such as processing cheese, recycling dyes and detergents and many more applications.

There are two different methods of constructing R/O membranes; hollow fiber and spiral wound. Most of the R/O membranes seen today are spiral wound. The maximum amount of permeate that can pass through a membrane without damaging it is 25 gallons per day per square foot of membrane. If this figure is exceeded the membrane will fail.

There are basically two different methods of increasing permeate (product), pressure and temperature. By raising the pressure or temperature the permeate will increase. By increasing the pressure through the adjustment of the flow restrictor the amount of permeate increases and is purer. The standard temperature that R/O membranes are tested at is 77 degrees F, by increasing the temperature as high as 120 degrees F the amount of permeate can be increased also. Two words of caution. First you must know both the temperature and pressure limitations of the membrane. Secondly do not over-restrict the concentrate to accomplish an increase in pressure, this will cause premature fouling of the membrane. And third NEVER close off the flow restrictor valve completely, it will not only destroy the membrane, but the pressure

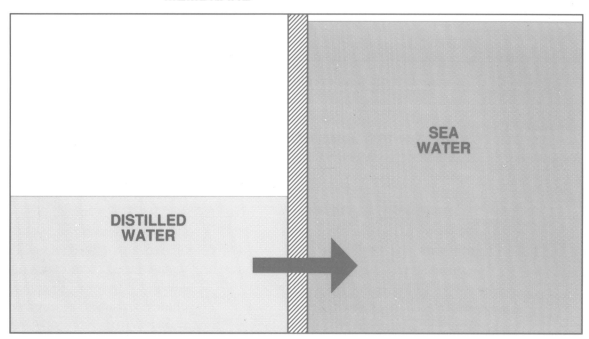

SEMI-PERMEABLE MEMBRANE

SEA WATER

DISTILLED WATER

OSMOSIS

EXAMPLE #1

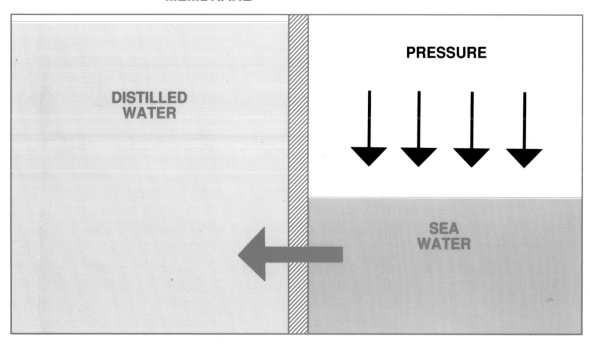

SEMI-PERMEABLE MEMBRANE

DISTILLED WATER

PRESSURE

SEA WATER

REVERSE OSMOSIS

EXAMPLE #2

membrane vessel may explode!

There are always three orifices on a reverse osmosis vessel. They are called feed (source; in water probably the tap water), permeate (in water it is often referred to as the product), and concentrate (reject).

Within a pressure vessel there can be anywhere from a single RO membrane to a large vessel with several membranes within one housing.

Reverse osmosis will remove heavy metals, radioactive particles, minerals, and also bacteria and viruses. It will remove up to 99% of some of these items but will not remove 100% of anything (We aren't talking about gravel folks!) And R/O cannot treat water with more than 70,000 ppm of salt. R/O cannot remove some solvents (but good GAC will).

Believe it or not the way the liquid passes through the membrane is still a mystery. Even under the highest magnification of an electron microscope there are NO pores in the membrane surface!

There is some variation in the quality and types of membrane as to what percentage of the contaminant is removed. A good membrane will remove from 96-98% of certain suspended contaminants. For instance take a feed water with 100 ppm TDS, the permeate will contain about 4 ppm TDS.

There are five types of RO membrane materials: 1. Polyamide (hollow fiber). The least common type found, probably will not concern you. 2. Diacetate or CA (cellulose based). 3. Triacetate or CTA (cellulose based) 4. Blend (99% of CA membranes) optimizes DI- and TRI- Acetate properties. 5. Thin Film Composite or TFC –

State of the Art for R/O.

Why is it necessary to know the different types of membranes? If you utilize the wrong membrane for a particular application, it will fail! We will lump all of the cellulose-based membranes together and refer to them as CA while the thin film composite membranes will be referred to as TFC.

IT IS VERY IMPORTANT TO UNDERSTAND ONE VERY BASIC FACT! CA membranes benefit from chlorine and chloramines in the feed water. These are organic based membranes; they are subject to microbial degradation. The chlorine reduces the number of microbes entering the membrane. On the other hand the TFC membranes will fail if subjected to chlorine or chloramines. For this reason TFC membranes are referred to as well water systems.

Reverse Osmosis membranes can come in an array of lengths and diameters. Membranes can be anything from 1 1/2 to 8" in diameter and from 6 to 60" in length. Only the smallest membranes do not require a pump. The highest pressure membrane can withstand pressures of 1200 psi.

There are a number of calculations that go into choosing the right system to fit your needs. Have your water analyzed and then contact a reputable R/O systems manufacturer so that you can be assured of getting the right equipment for your application. There are also several ads in *Tropical Fish Hobbyist* magazine of companies selling these units, again including Feiller Fisheries.

Check out the R/O industry to be certain that you purchase the product that is going to provide the

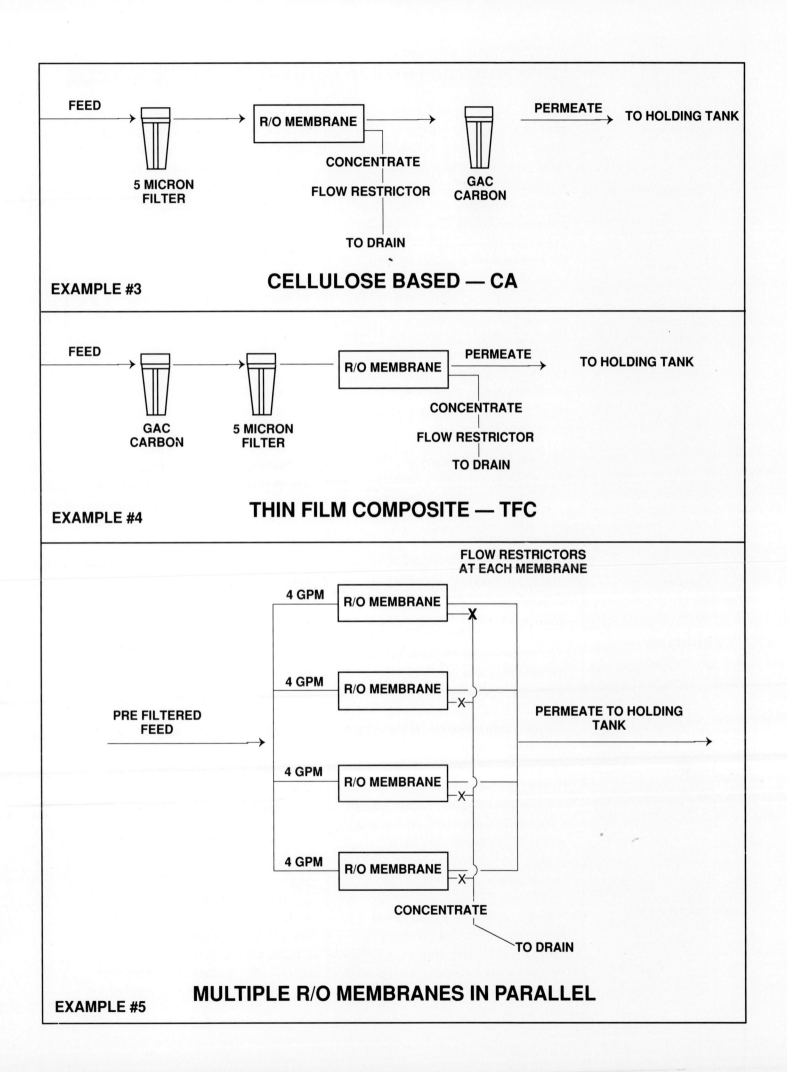

FEED

5 MICRON
FILTER

R/O MEMBRANE

CONCENTRATE

FLOW RESTRICTOR

TO DRAIN

GAC
CARBON

PERMEATE TO HOLDING TANK

CELLULOSE BASED — CA

EXAMPLE #3

FEED

GAC
CARBON

5 MICRON
FILTER

R/O MEMBRANE

PERMEATE

TO HOLDING TANK

CONCENTRATE

FLOW RESTRICTOR

TO DRAIN

THIN FILM COMPOSITE — TFC

EXAMPLE #4

**FLOW RESTRICTORS
AT EACH MEMBRANE**

4 GPM R/O MEMBRANE X

4 GPM R/O MEMBRANE X

4 GPM R/O MEMBRANE X

4 GPM R/O MEMBRANE X

**PRE FILTERED
FEED**

**PERMEATE TO HOLDING
TANK**

CONCENTRATE

TO DRAIN

MULTIPLE R/O MEMBRANES IN PARALLEL

EXAMPLE #5

right system for your particular application. The inexpensive 10 gpd unit may, in the long run, be the most expensive unit you can buy, if you have an emergency where a lot of water is needed and your fish are acclimated to R/O. The loss of fish from such an incident can in value far exceed what a proper system would have cost you.

There are several different ways that an R/O system can be designed. Whether you are looking at a 10 gpd (gallons per day) unit or a 10,000,000 gpd system the same principles apply. And these principles are what we are going to go into some depth on.

REVERSE OSMOSIS SYSTEMS:

Different ways that R/O membranes can be utilized in a system.

Example #3. A standard small system with one R/O membrane, one particulate filter, usually 5 micron, and one GAC membrane. The particulate filter and the GAC elements are housed in the typical 10" housings that are found everywhere. The R/O membrane itself is housed in a small length of pvc pipe with some custom end caps and fittings. These units with CA membranes usually don't go above 15 gpd, but most produce much less.

Example #4. This is a diagram of a Thin Film Composite membrane system. Notice that the GAC module is ahead of the membrane, just the opposite of the CA membrane.

Example #5. This is a typical system where several membranes run in parallel. The advantage to this type of set up is that the quality of permeate or product is constantly the highest. The disadvantages of this set up is that each membrane can recover about 15% of the feed water as permeate. So 85% of the water is discharged as concentrate reject. The second disadvantage is the amount of water necessary for the proper functioning of the membranes. The third is that all of the pre-filtration processes must be increased proportionately to compensate for the increased feed water. Remember the limits of GAC. The amount of GAC must increase proportionately.

Example #6. This a typical system with several membranes run in series. There are several advantages to this system. First of all the same amount of feed can handle several membranes in series. (The calculations for delta-p drop across the membrane and the loss of feed water due to the permeate in the preceding membranes has to be carefully worked out). The same size GAC tank and prefilter elements can handle as many as 6 membranes in series.

The disadvantage is that with each consecutive membrane the quality of permeate is lower. Remember that each membrane recovers about 15% of the feed as permeate and the concentrate increases in osmotic pressure and density. So if the first membrane is looking at water of 1000 ppm the second membrane is looking at water with a total dissolved solids of 1150 ppm and then the next even higher and so on.

Most water sources are in the 100 to 400 ppm TDS range so the small amount of TDS is not a problem. Discus will successfully spawn and produce fry in water much harder than 100 ppm. A combination of

R/O and GAC have removed the toxic substances.

Example #7. To obtain the most recovery from an R/O system is through the recycling and mixing of the concentrate with new water. This can be done with the membranes in parallel or in series. Having the membranes in series is the best way to conserve the quantity of feed, prefilters and GAC required.

Depending on the quality of your water, as much 93% of the feed water can be recovered. This along with a very high production rate can equal a DI in production without the constant recharging of the resins. An R/O system runs day and night for days on end without service. Adding a storage vessel to your fish room is an excellent way to maintain a large amount of reserved purified water. This same principle is applicable to small systems as to large systems. A pump always has to be utilized for recycling.

The biggest negative attributed to R/O is wasted water. I have a 1200 gpd recycling system where I have about a 90% recovery for the fish and the remaining 10% or so goes into the yard. Never down the drain.

To construct a recycling system the following equipment shown in the diagram is all that is needed. As with all RO systems it is a good idea to also include flow gauges, and meters to monitor TDS and pH within the system.

WORDS OF CAUTION ABOUT WATER THAT IS TOO PURE. Because of the combination of GAC and R/O the water is even stripped too much for the Discus so that the addition of some trace elements or peat extract is beneficial.

Second, by stripping the water of all the alkali buffers also creates a problem. The water becomes very unstable and the pH can drop 2 full numbers in twenty four hours. A good pH and hardness meter is a must. Myronl of Carlsbad, California makes some excellent small units. If you are unable to afford a good meter then use good quality regents like those manufactured by Hach Company. Cheap reagents are just as inaccurate as cheap meters. To stabilize the pH it may be necessary to add a little baking soda to the water to raise the Micromhos to around 50.

MAINTENANCE: To insure that the membrane can have a long life of up to 4 years or more it is advisable to wash the membrane with either acids (such as citric acid), alkalis or special detergents. These chemicals can be purchased from a chemical supply house or from a company such as Applied Membranes of San Marcos, California. Applied membranes will send you the right chemicals for the problems that you describe plus instructions on how to clean the membranes.

Yes, it is necessary to use harsh chemicals with R/O, too, but instead of every few hundred gallons it need only be every so many thousands of gallons.

DESCALENTS:

Reverse osmosis systems were designed to desalinate. In systems where fresh water is used it is normally run through a Cation resin water softener where the exchange of mineral ions to sodium ions takes place. The sodium ions will not scale on the surface of the membrane whereas the calcium carbonates will.

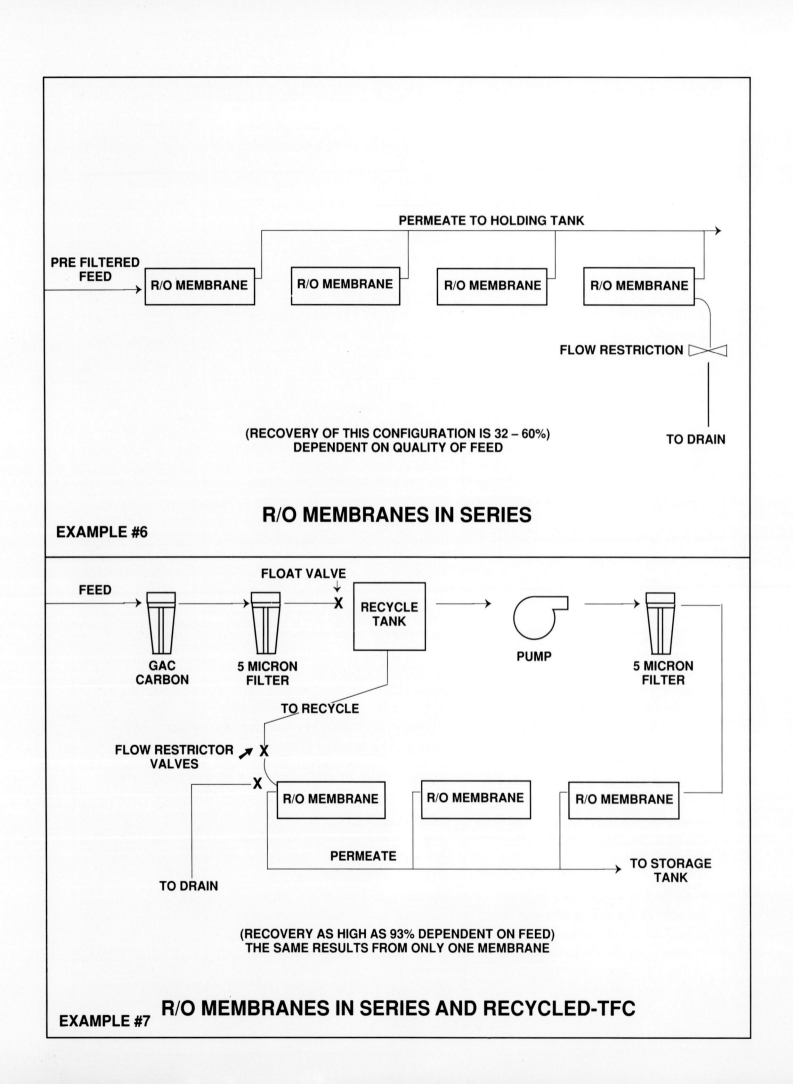

PERMEATE TO HOLDING TANK

PRE FILTERED FEED

R/O MEMBRANE   R/O MEMBRANE   R/O MEMBRANE   R/O MEMBRANE

FLOW RESTRICTION

TO DRAIN

(RECOVERY OF THIS CONFIGURATION IS 32 – 60%)
DEPENDENT ON QUALITY OF FEED

R/O MEMBRANES IN SERIES

EXAMPLE #6

FLOAT VALVE

FEED

GAC CARBON   5 MICRON FILTER   RECYCLE TANK   PUMP   5 MICRON FILTER

TO RECYCLE

FLOW RESTRICTOR VALVES

R/O MEMBRANE   R/O MEMBRANE   R/O MEMBRANE

PERMEATE   TO STORAGE TANK

TO DRAIN

(RECOVERY AS HIGH AS 93% DEPENDENT ON FEED)
THE SAME RESULTS FROM ONLY ONE MEMBRANE

R/O MEMBRANES IN SERIES AND RECYCLED-TFC

EXAMPLE #7

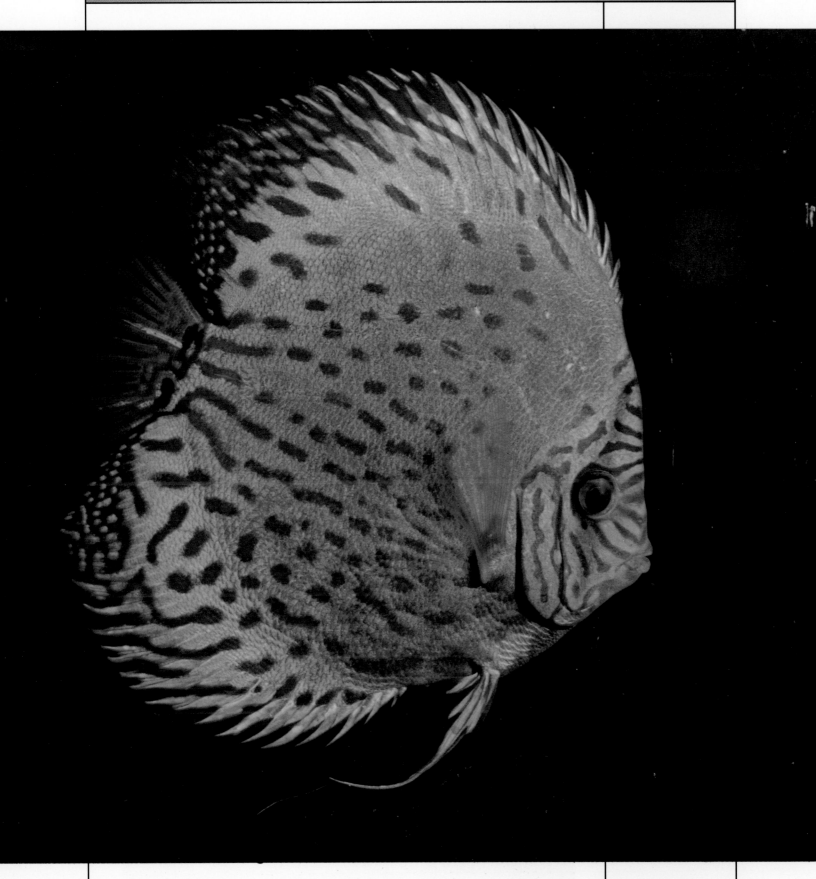

A nice example of
Gan's turquoise.

There are two other methods of preventing scale fouling of the membranes, the first being anti-scalents which are chemicals manufactured just for that purpose and the second method is with a catalytic unit that neutralizes the charges of ions of the water going through it. The latter is the method that I use and appear to have good success with it. The one I use is manufactured by Free Flow.

I do not use a cation resin water softener because of the salt poured down the drain and the wasted recycling of water. Several million gallons a week alone are wasted in the San Francisco Bay Area due to water softeners. Besides the waste, water management plants have to contend with all of that salt.

Water is a precious, precious resource. Probably the most precious. There is no new water being miraculously poured out of the sky by God. All of the water has been recycled millions and perhaps billions of times. So how we take care of it now will have a direct bearing on how good it will be for our children and grandchildren. I feel that it is the responsibility of each inhabitant of this planet to defend the right of water to be pure.

To balance the water purification picture, water being poured down the drain should also be treated. Never use medications in the shotgun approach when you do not know what you are treating. Use medications only when you have a fairly accurate diagnosis and know which medication will be effective.

If you should use medications, dyes, etc. run the water through GAC and than down the drain. Help the environment by not adding to the resistant strains of disease causing organisms. Be a responsible fish keeper.

C.W. Wong's cobalts.

List of Respondents:

Au, Dicklam
55 Riverton Drive
San Francisco, CA 94132

Chan, Dr. Clifford
6 Jalan Pandan
1128 Singapore

Dollman, David
205 N. State Street
Marengo, IL 60152

Richard Feiller
554 Gaundeberg Lane
San Jose, CA 95136

Gobel, Manfred
D-6101 Rossdorf 2
Stetteritzning 7
Germany

Handley, Donald
76 Park Road
Titirangi, Auckland 7
New Zealand

Jordan, Dale
71 Melon Lea Cover
Winnipeg, Manitoba
Canada R2G 2L4

Long, Stephen
4 Heathfield Crescent
Northend
Bulawayo
Zimbabwe

Nakamura, Yasushi
8-48 Yatsu 4-Chome
Narashino, Chiba 275
Japan

Reeves, Dr. Kenneth, DVM
8085 Owens Way
Arvada, Colorado 80005

Schmidt-Focke, Dr. Eduard
6380 Bad Homburg
Langenfeld 10
Germany

Schulze, Eberhard
The Highgate Aquarist
367 A Archway Road
London, N64 EJ
England

Shirase, Akimitsu
c/o Hirose Tropicals Ltd.
8-48 Yatsu 4 Chome
Narashino, Chiba 275
Japan

Wong, Chong Moh
I-J, Thean Teik Road
Ayer Itam, Penang
Malaysia 1140

In closing, I would like to thank all the respondents whose valuable information I've used here. Their assemblage of opinions and ideas has made my work easy. Again, I say, "mil gracias."

Jack H. Wattley

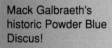

Mack Galbraeth's historic Powder Blue Discus!

Index

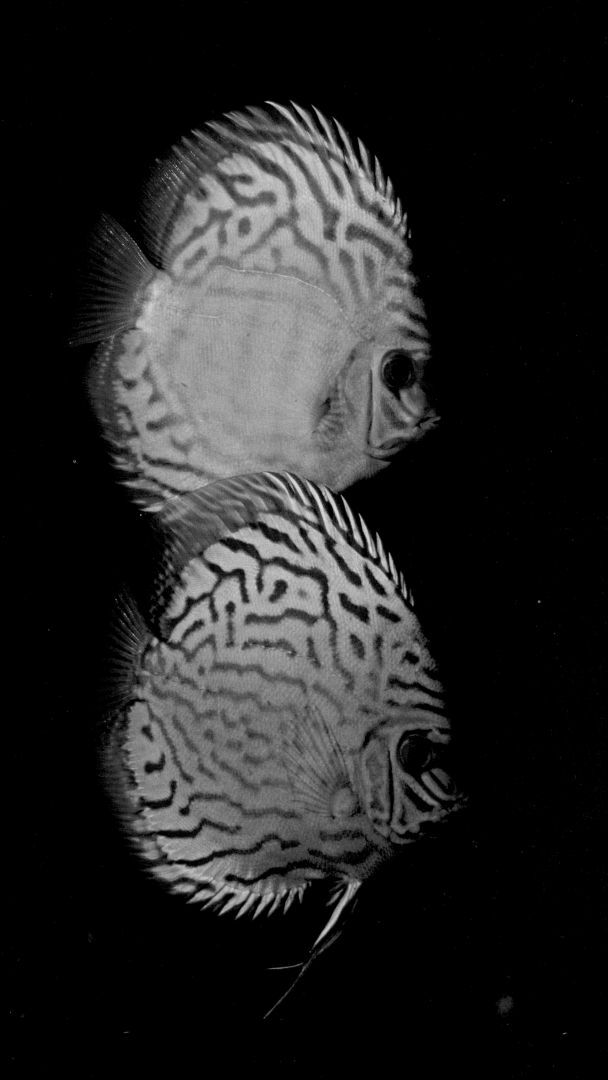

These discus were
raised in Singapore
at the Gan
Aquarium Fish Farm
and were derived
from turquoise
stock originally
produced by Jack
Wattley. Photo
courtesy of Dr.
Clifford Chan.

JACK WATTLEY
DISCUS
FOR THE PERFECTIONIST